TAGALOG PICTURE DICTIONARY COLORING BOOK

Over 1500 Tagalog Words and Phrases for Creative & Visual Learners of All Ages

Color and Learn

Lingo Mastery

ISBN: 978-1-951949-67-9

Free Book Reveals The 6-Step Blueprint That Took Students **From Language Learners To Fluent In 3 Months**

- **6 Unbelievable Hacks** that will accelerate your learning curve

- **Mind Training:** Why memorizing vocabulary is easy

- **One Hack to Rule Them All:** This <u>secret nugget</u> will blow you away...

Head over to **LingoMastery.com/hacks** and claim your free book now!

CONTENTS

INTRODUCTION

This Tagalog Picture Dictionary Coloring Book is a fun vocabulary-building tool with illustrations that you can color while studying. It covers an immense range of topics that will help you learn everything related to the Tagalog language in daily subjects, from members of the family and animals to parts of the body and describing jobs.

This introduction is a guide to help you get started in Tagalog and polish your basic grammar, spelling, punctuation, and vocabulary skills. Good luck – and **most importantly, enjoy yourself!**

BASICS OF THE TAGALOG LANGUAGE

I. Spelling and Pronunciation

a. The Tagalog Alphabet – A Built-in Guide to Pronunciation.

There are certain letters that you pronounce differently in your native language and in Tagalog. Some letters may not even exist in your language. You must therefore learn to recognize these letters and pronounce them correctly.

A (*ey*)	H (*eyts*)	Ñ (*enye*)	T (*ti*)
B (*bi*)	I (*ay*)	Ng (*endzi*)	U (*yu*)
C (*si*)	J (*dzey*)	O (*o*)	V (*vi*)
D (*di*)	K (*key*)	P (*pi*)	W (*dobolyu*)
E (*i*)	L (*el*)	Q (*kyu*)	X (*eks*)
F (*ef*)	M (*em*)	R (*ar*)	Y (*way*)
G (*dzi*)	N (*en*)	S (*es*)	Z (*zi*)

To improve your pronunciation, you must also learn to pronounce letter combinations, such as "ng," "dy," "sy," "ts" ...

b. Pronunciation

The best way to acquire a good Tagalog pronunciation is to listen, as often as you can, to movies or radio broadcasts. You will notice that Tagalog contains several nasal sounds that are not used in English, which can only be learned by listening and imitating. Here is a quick guide of how to pronounce the most common letter combinations:

Vowels

The Tagalog alphabet has 5 vowels:

A -> sounds like *a* -> as in *fat*

E -> sounds like *e* -> as in *bed*

I -> sounds like *i* -> as in *big*

O -> sounds like *o* -> as in *old*

U -> sounds like *u* -> as in *super*

Consonants

While there are 23 consonants in the Tagalog alphabet, here are the 15 basic ones. These consonants were in the earlier Tagalog alphabet named as **Abakada.** In the 1980s, 8 consonants from the English alphabet were added to the modern alphabet of Tagalog and they are generally used for proper nouns.

B -> sounds like *ba* -> as in *bag*

D-> sounds like *da* -> as in *dash*

G -> sounds like *ga* -> as in *gang*

H -> sounds like *ha* -> as in *ham*

K -> sounds like *ka-* > as in *karate*

L -> sounds like *la* -> as in *lamb*

M -> sounds like *ma* -> as in *mat*

N -> sounds like *na* -> as in *nap*

NG -> sounds like *nga* -> as in **ngayon** (*Tagalog word - meaning now*)

P -> sounds like *pa* -> as in *pan*

R -> sounds like *ra* -> as in *rat*

S -> sounds like *sa* -> as in *sand*

T -> sounds like *ta* -> as in *tap*

W -> sounds like *wa*-> as in *watch*

Y -> sounds like *ya* -> as in *yank*

A few more rules

- In Tagalog, the five vowels are pronounced with a short-vowel sound: short-a, short-e, short-i, short-o, and short-u.

- In the Tagalog alphabet, there are no silent vowels.
- For vowels that are next to each other, they are pronounced separately.
  Examples: aa (*a-a*), ai (*a-i*), ao (*a-o*), oo (*o-o*), uo (*oo-o*)

- The majority of the consonants are pronounced the same as they are pronounced in English, except for the following:
  - Ñ -> pronounced as Ñ (*n + y*) in Spanish -> as in **Señor** meaning *Mr.* or *Sir*
  - R -> pronounced as rolled R -> as in **rosas** (RO-sas) meaning *rose*
  - DY -> pronounced as *j* -> as in **dyip** (DYIP) meaning *jeepney*
  - TS -> pronounced as *ch* -> as in **tsaa** (tsa-A) meaning *tea*

Grammar – Verbs and Tenses

I-   Glossary

<u>Verb</u>: A doing word. It describes an <u>action.</u>

<u>Tense</u>: It tells you <u>when</u> an action happens/happened/will happen, etc.

<u>Subject</u>: It refers to <u>who</u> is doing the action. There will be a different ending for each person.

singular	ako	*I*
	ikaw/ka	*you (informal)*
	siya	*he/she*
plural	tayo	*we*
	kayo	*you (formal and group)*
	sila	*they*

<u>Ending</u>: Usually the last two letters in a word, it will tell you what tense you are in and what person you are using.

<u>Stem/Root</u>: It's what is left of the verb once the ending is gone OR it is the part you will be using from the verb's infinitive form.

<u>Infinitive</u>: The only form of the verb you will find in the dictionary.

<u>Regular verbs</u>: Verbs that always follow standard patterns.

<u>Irregular verbs</u>: Verbs that does not follow a pattern OR have an irregular root.

<u>Auxiliary verbs</u>: In Tagalog, the most common auxiliary verb is **maaari.**

Maaari	Can/May
Maaaring ako	*I can/may*
Maaaring ka	*You (singular) can/may*
Maaaring siya	*He/She can/may*
Maaaring tayo	*We can/may*
Maaaring kayo	*You (plural) can/may*
Maaaring sila	*They can/may*

Affixes: Tagalog verbs are formed using *affixes,* or **mga panlapi,** to show the tense. Theses affixes may be placed at the beginning (*prefixes* or **mga unlapi**), middle (*infixes* or **mga gitlapi**), and end (*suffixes* or hulapi) of the word. Here are the common affixes used:

Mga Unlapi *(Prefixes)*	Mga Gitlapi *(Infixes)*	Mga Hulapi *(Suffixes)*
mag	um	an
ma	in	

II. Verb Tenses

The verbs in Tagalog have three (3) tenses – *past* or **pangnagdaan,** *present* or **pangkasalukuyan,** and *future* or **panghinaharap.** But they are different from English as certain rules are followed to suit the tense. Among them are:

- Adjusting the affix
- Repeating the first syllable of the root word
- Changing the vowel of the root word, like from *O* to *U*
- Dropping some letters of the root word

A. The Past Tense

The verb is in the past tense if the action has been done already.

1. How to build it

- Use an affix and adjust it when needed, then add to the root word.

Examples:

Panlapi (*Affix*)	Salitang-ugat (*Root word*)	Pangnagdaan (*Past Tense*)
um	tawa (*laugh*)	tumawa (*laughed*)
nag	salita (*talk*)	nagsalita (*talked*)
na	ayos (*fix*)	naayos (*fixed*)
in	bigkas (*pronounce*)	binigkas (*pronounced*)

ATTENTION:

- The affix **um** is added before the first letter of the verb that starts with a vowel. If the first letter of the verb starts with a consonant, **um** is placed after it.
  Examples:

  > **um + alis** (*leave*) -> **umalis** (*left*)
  > **bili** (*buy*) **+ um** -> **bumili** (*bought*)

- Some affixes will be adjusted (e.g., **mag->nag**).
  Examples:

  > **mag + sayaw** (*dance*) -> **nagsayaw** (*danced*)

2. Use of the past tense

- To say what happened or what has been done already (e.g., last year, yesterday, this morning).
- To say what has been happening for a period of time or continuously, since a particular time and is still happening.

B. The Present Tense

The verb is in the present tense if the action, movement, or event is happening.

1. How to build it

- Use an affix and adjust it when needed, then repeat the first syllable of the root word.

Examples:

Panlapi (*Affix*)	Salitang-ugat (*Root word*)	Pangkasalukuyan (*Present Tense*)
um	awit (*sing*)	umaawit (*singing*)
mag	basa (*read*)	nagbabasa (*reading*)
ma	tuto (*learn*)	natututo (*learning*)
in	timbang (*weigh*)	tinitimbang (*weighing*)

ATTENTION:

- Some affixes will be adjusted (e.g., **mag->nag**)
  Examples:

  mag + luto (*cook*) **-> nagluluto** (*cooking*)

2. Uses of the present tense

- To say what happens repeatedly (e.g., every year, every day, every morning).
- To say what is happening now or at the present time.
- To say what regularly happens.
- To say what has been happening for a period of time or continuously, since a particular time and is still happening.

C. The Future Tense

The verb is in the future tense if the action has not happened or has not been done yet.

1. How to build it

Some words may not need an affix, while some may use it, then repeat the first syllable of the root word.

Examples:

Panlapi *(Affix)*	Salitang-ugat *(Root word)*	Panghinaharap *(Future Tense)*
(no affix)	**lukso** *(jump)*	**lulukso** *(will jump)*
mag	**dala** *(bring)*	**magdadala** *(will bring)*
ma	**ligo** *(take a bath)*	**maliligo** *(will take a bath)*
in	**hati** *(divide)*	**hahatiin** *(will divide)*
an	**hugas** *(wash)*	**huhugasan** *(will wash)*

ATTENTION:

- The affixes **mag** and **ma** will not be changed to **nag** and **na,** respectively.
  Examples:
  > **mag + lakbay** *(travel)* -> **maglalakbay** *(will travel)*
  > **ma + buo** *(form)* -> **mabubuo** *(will be formed)*

- The affix **um** is not used for the future tense.
- Verbs ending in **O** or those with **O** before ending in consonant letters will be changed to **U** plus the affix for this particular tense.
  Examples:

Salitang Ugat *(Root Word)*	Panghinaharap *(Future Tense)*
halo *(mix)*	**hahaluin** *(will mix)*
salo *(catch)*	**sasaluhin** *(will catch)*
sundo *(fetch or pick up)*	**susunduin** *(will fetch or pick up)*
libot *(go around)*	**lilibutin** *(will go around)*
sagot *(answer)*	**sasagutin** *(will answer)*
tanong *(ask)*	**tatanungin** *(will ask)*

2. Use of the future tense

- To say what will be done (e.g., later, next time, tomorrow, the next day, someday).

Infinitive Verb

An infinitive verb is the base or unconjugated form of a verb that can be used in several ways, as it functions as a noun, adjective, and adverb. The word "*to*" is used in front of an infinitive verb.

Examples:

Infinitive Verb	**Pawatas na Pandiwa**
to hide	itago
to borrow	manghiram
to sweep	walisan
to hug	yakapin
to say	sabihin

Noun

A noun refers to a person, thing, place, animal, plant, idea, or event.

Examples:

tao *(person)*	**Edward, ate** *(older sister),* **ama** *(father),* **doktor** *(doctor),* **guro** *(teacher)*
bagay *(thing)*	**lapis** *(pencil),* **aklat** *(book),* **mesa** *(table),* **liham** *(letter),* **plato** *(plate)*
lugar *(place)*	**tahanan** *(home),* **paaralan** *(school),* **palengke** *(market),* **Maynila** *(Manila),* **Pilipinas** *(Philippines)*
hayop *(animal)*	**aso** *(dog),* **pusa** *(cat),* **daga** *(mouse),* **tigre** *(tiger),* **isda** *(fish)*
halaman *(plant)*	**puno** *(tree),* **rosas** *(rose),* **ubas** *(grape),* **niyog** *(coconut),* **lagundi** *(shrub)*
ideya *(idea)*	**pagmamahal** *(love),* **kapayapaan** *(peace),* **kapangyarihan** *(power),* **pagkakaibigan** *(friendship),* **karunungan** *(wisdom)*
pangyayari *(event)*	**piyesta** *(feast),* **Pasko** *(Christmas),* **Kwaresma** *(Lent),* **paligsahan** *(contest),* **halalan** *(election)*

A. Types of Nouns

1. Common and Proper Nouns

Common nouns, or **pangngalang pambalana,** name persons, things, places, ideas, or events that are generic. Unless it is placed at the beginning of a sentence, this type of noun is not capitalized. Proper nouns, or **pangngalang pantangi,** are the names of particular persons, things, places, ideas, or events. They start with capital letters.

Examples:

	Pangngalang pambalana (Common noun)	Pangngalang pantangi (Proper noun)
tao (person)	**bayani** (hero)	Jose Rizal
bagay (thing)	**sapatos** (shoes)	Nike
lugar (place)	**bansa** (country)	New Zealand
ideya (idea)	**relihiyon** (religion)	Islam
pangyayari (event)	**pista** (festival)	Ati-Atihan

2. Singular and Plural Nouns

Singular nouns mean only one, while plural nouns mean more than one. Here are the rules to make a singular noun plural.

a. For most common nouns, <u>s</u> is added to make it plural. Examples: *dog->dogs, flag->flags,*

b. For some nouns ending in *f* or <u>*fe,*</u> <u>s</u> may be added. In some words, *f* needs to be changed to <u>v</u> and <u>es</u> is added. Examples: *roof->roofs, giraffe->giraffes, leaf->leaves*

c. For nouns ending in <u>s, ss, sh, ch, x,</u> add <u>es.</u> Examples: *bus->buses, glass->glasses, wish->wishes, peach->peaches, fox->foxes*

d. For those ending in <u>z</u>, add another <u>z</u> and then add <u>es</u>. Examples: *quiz->quizzes, buzz->buzzes*

ATTENTION:

In Tagalog, there are three grammatical number of nouns or **kailanan ng pangangalan** – **isahan** (*singular*), **dalawahan** (*dual*), and **maramihan** (*plural*). Article/case marker or **pananda** is placed before a noun. "Mga" is commonly used to indicate that a noun is in its plural form. However, native Tagalog speakers distinguish dalawahan (dual) by using "kapwa" or "mag" instead of "mga."

When "mag" is used as a case marker and the first syllable of the noun is repeated, *dalawahan* is then transformed to *maramihan*.

		Isahan *(Singular)*	Dalawahan *(Dual)*	Maramihan *(Plural)*
before the common noun or **pangngalang pambala**		**ang** aso *(dog)* **ng** bahay *(house)*	**ang mga** aso *(dogs)* **ng mga** bahay *(houses)*	
			magkapitbahay *(two neighbors)* **mag**kaibigan *(two friends)*	**mag**kakapitbahay *(neighbors)* **mag**kakaibigan *(friends)*
			kapwa guro *(two teachers)* **kapwa** ina *(two mothers)*	
before the proper noun or **panggalang pantangi**		**Si** Jose Rizal	**Sina** Jose Rizal at Andres Bonifacio	**Sina** Jose Rizal, Andres Bonifacio, Marcelo del Pilar, Apolinario Mabini at Emilio Aguinaldo
		Ni Andrea	**Ni** Andrea at Romana	**Ni** Andrea, Romana at Luisa
		Kay Gng. Barba	**Kay** Gng. Barba at Bb. Garcia	**Kay** Gng. Barba, Bb. Garcia, G. Mortez at G. Ocampo

3. Masculine, Feminine, Common and Neuter Nouns

In English, there are four categories of gender nouns - masculine, feminine, common, and neuter. Tagalog has the same categories and are named as **panlalaki, pambabae, di-tiyak,** and **walang kasarian**, respectively.

Examples:

Panlalaki *(masculine)*	Pambabae *(feminine)*	Di-tiyak *(common)*	Walang Kasarian *(neuter)*
lolo (grandfather)	**tiya** *(aunt)*	**guro** *(teacher)*	**laruan** *(toy)*

Adjective

An adjective, or **pang-uri,** describes, identifies, or defines a noun and pronoun. It may be seen before the noun or after a linking verb. In Tagalog, it may come after the linker **ay**.

Examples: **Nakatanggap siya ng <u>malaking</u> manika.** *(She received a <u>big</u> doll.)*

Si Juan ay <u>matangkad</u>. *(John is <u>tall</u>.)*

A. Forms of Adjectives

1. Simple

This form is the most basic kind of adjective, also sometimes known as "positive" adjective.

2. Comparative

This is used to compare two nouns, where *-er* for a single syllable adjective and *more* for two-syllable or more adjective may be used.

3. Superlative

This is used to describe a noun which is at the upper or lower limit of the quality level. Sometimes, a noun is compared to a group and *-est* for a single syllable adjective and *most* for two-syllable or more adjective may be used.

ATTENTION:

- In Tagalog, simple adjectives are known as **lantay na pang-uri.**

- Comparative adjectives, or **pahambing na pang-uri** in Tagalog, may have similar and dissimilar adjectives where the following words, terms, or syllables are used:

Magkatulad *(Similar)*	Di-magkatulad *(Dissimilar)*
ka- kasin- /kasing- /kasim magkasin- /magkasing- /magkasim- magsin- / magsing- /magsim- kapwa	di-tulad higit na mas...kaysa di-lubhang di-gaanong

- Superlative adjectives, or **pasukdol na pang-uri** in Tagalog, use the following: **pinaka-, napaka- , sakdal-, ubod nang, hari ng.**

Examples:

Lantay na Pang-uri *(Simple Adjective)*	Pahambing na Pang-uri *(Comparative Adjective)*	Pasukdol na Pang-uri *(Superlative Adjective)*
masaya *(happy)*	**mas masaya** *(happier)*	**pinakamasaya** *(happiest)*
mabilis *(fast)*	**higit na mabilis** *(faster)*	**pinakamabilis** *(fastest)*
matapang *(brave)*	**mas matapang** *(braver)*	**pinakamatapang** *(bravest)*
masarap *(delicious)*	**mas masarap** *(more delicious)*	**pinakamasarap** *(most delicious)*
madali *(easy)*	**higit na madali** *(easier)*	**pinakamadali** *(easiest)*

Adverb

An adverb, or **pang-abay** in Tagalog, is a word that describes a verb, an adjective, or another adverb. Often, it is used to describe a frequency, time, place, manner, or degree.

ATTENTION:

- The adverb in Tagalog that describes time is called **pang-abay na pamanahon**.
  Examples: **kahapon** *(yesterday)*, **araw-araw** *(everyday)*

- The Tagalog adverb that shows the place where an action is done is called **pang-abay na panlunan**.
  Examples: **sa paaralan** *(in school)*, **sa palasyo** *(in the palace)*

Final Notes

Please bear in mind that this initial section is a way of introducing the Tagalog language. Said language has its complex aspects, but can still be easy and very exciting to learn. Reading and understanding the basics of the Tagalog Language are indeed a good foundation.

Moreover, it is important to let you know that the succeeding parts will teach you more about the Tagalog words with their pronunciation and corresponding translation in the English language. Answering the quizzes will also give you the chance to test yourself and prove what you have discovered. So, good luck on your learning experience!

MGA DAMDAMIN (EMOTIONS)

1) **masayá** (happy)
   ma-sa-YA

2) **malungkót** (sad)
   ma-lung-KOT

3) **nasasabík** (excited)
   na-sa-sa-BIK

4) **galít** (angry)
   ga-LIT

5) **nagúlat** (surprised)
   na-GU-lat

6) **nagmamalasákit** (concerned)
   nag-ma-ma-la-SA-kit

7) **takót** (scared)
   ta-KOT

8) **mausísa** (curious)
   ma-u-SI-sa

9) **nalilibáng** (amused)
   na-li-li-BANG

10) **nalilíto** (confused)
    na-li-LI-to

11) **maysakít** (sick)
    may-sa-KIT

12) **pílyo** (naughty)
    PIL-yo

13) **seryóso** (serious)
    ser-YO-so

14) **nakatutók** (focused)
    na-ka-tu-TOK

15) **nababagót** (bored)
    na-ba-ba-GOT

16) **nagúguluhan** (overwhelmed)
    na-GU-gu-lu-han

17) **umiíbig** (in love)
    u-mi-I-big

18) **nahihiyâ** (ashamed)
    na-hi-hi-YA

19) **nababalisá** (anxious)
    na-ba-ba-li-SA

20) **nasusuklám** (disgusted)
    na-su-suk-LAM

21) **nasasaktán** (offended)
    na-sa-sak-TAN

22) **naghihírap** (sore)
    nag-hi-HI-RAP

Galit siya sa iyo.
He is angry at you.

Ang aking lolo at lola ay umiibig pa rin nang husto.
My grandparents are still very much in love.

Nagkasakit ako dahil sa pagkain kahapon.
Yesterday's meal made me sick.

ANG PAMILYA (THE FAMILY)

1) **lólo't lóla** (grandparents)
LO-lot LO-la

2) **lóla** (grandmother)
LO-la

3) **lólo** (grandfather)
LO-lo

4) **tíyo** (uncle)
TI-yo

5) **iná** (mother)
i-NA

6) **amá** (father)
a-MA

7) **tíya** (aunt)
TI-ya

8) **pínsang laláki** (cousin, m.)
PIN-sang-la-LA-ki

9) **kapatíd na laláki** (brother)
ka-pa-TID-na-la-LA-ki

10) **akó** (me)
a-KO

11) **asáwang laláki/ babáe** (husband/wife)
a-SA-wang-la-LA-ki/ba-BA-e

12) **kapatíd na babáe** (sister)
ka-pa-TID-na-ba-BA-e

13) **pínsang babáe** (cousin, f.)
PIN-sang-ba-BA-e

14) **pamangkíng laláki** (nephew)
pa-mang-KING-la-LA-ki

15) **anák na laláki** (*son*)
a-NAK-na-la-LA-ki

16) **anák na babáe** (daughter)
a-NAK-na-ba-BA-e

17) **pamangkíng babáe** (niece)
pa-mang-KING-ba-BA-e

18) **apóng laláki** (grandson)
a-PONG-la-LA-ki

19) **apóng babáe** (granddaughter)
a-PONG-ba-BA-e

20) **pangalawáng pínsan** (second cousin)
pa-nga-la-WANG-PIN-san

- **Mga Pinagbiyenan (In-laws)
– Mga Kamag-Anak (Relatives)**
ma-NGA-pi-nag-bi-ye-NAN
– ma-NGA-ka-mag-A-nak

21) **biyenáng laláki** (father-in-law)
bi-ye-NANG-la-LA-ki

22) **biyenáng babáe** (mother-in-law)
bi-ye-NANG-ba-BA-e

23) **bayáw** (brother-in-law)
ba-YAW

24) **hipág** (sister-in-law)
hi-PAG

25) **manúgang na babáe** (daughter-in-law)
ma-NU-gang-na-ba-BA-e

26) **manúgang na laláki** (son-in-law)
ma-NU-gang-na-la-LA-ki

27) **tiyuhín sa pamamagítan ng kasál**
(uncle-in-law)
ti-yu-HIN-sa-pa-ma-ma-GI-tan-ng-ka-SAL

28) **tiyahín sa pamamagítan ng kasál**
(aunt-in-law)
ti-ya-HIN-sa-pa-ma-ma-GI-tan-ng-ka-SAL

Anak ka talaga ng iyong ama!
You really are your father's daughter!

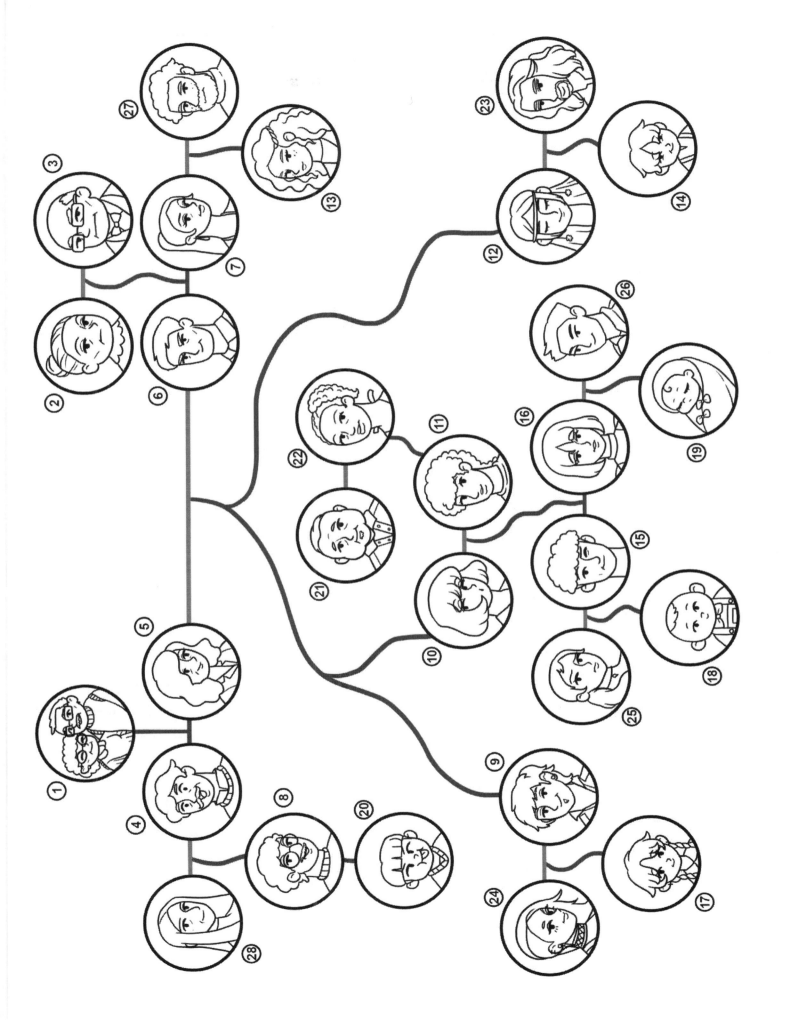

MGA RELASYON (RELATIONSHIPS)

1) **mag-asáwa** (married couple)
mag-a-SA-wa

2) **laláking may-asáwa** (married man)
la-LA-king-may-a-SA-wa

3) **babáeng may-asáwa** (married woman)
ba-BA-eng-may-a-SA-wa

4) **naghiwaláy na mag-asáwa** (divorced couple)
nag-hi-wa-LAY-na-mag-a-SA-wa

5) **dáting asáwang babáe** (ex-wife)
DA-ting-a-SA-wang-ba-BA-e

6) **dáting asáwang laláki** (ex-husband)
DA-ting-a-SA-wang-la-LA-ki

7) **kaibígan** (friend)
ka-i-BI-gan

8) **nóbya** (girlfriend)
NOB-ya

9) **nóbyo** (boyfriend)
NOB-yo

10) **kápitbáhay** (neighbor)
KA-pit-BA-hay

11) **waláng asáwa** (single)
wa-LANG-a-SA-wa

12) **diborsiyada** (divorcée/divorcé)
di-bor-si-YA-da

13) **biyúdo** (widower)
bi-YU-do

14) **biyúda** (widow)
bi-YU-da

Si Pauline ay may bagong kasintahang lalaki.
Pauline has a new boyfriend.

Wala pa akong asawa mula noong nakaraang taon.
I have been single since last year.

Ang aking kapitbahay ay lubhang mausisa.
My neighbor is very curious.

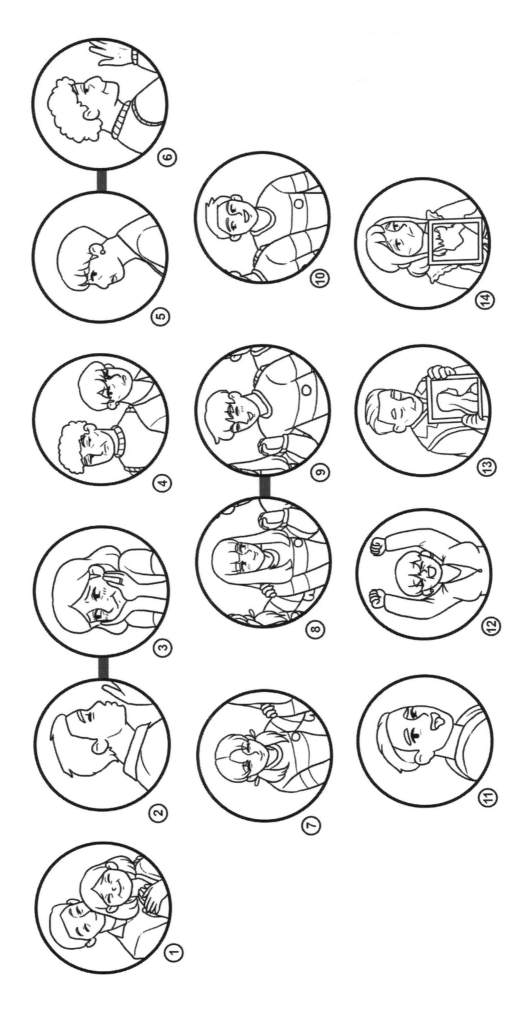

MGA ASAL (VALUES)

1) **paggálang** (respect)
   pag-GA-lang

2) **pasasalámat** (gratitude)
   pa-sa-sa-LA-mat

3) **pagpaparayà** (tolerance)
   pag-pa-pa-ra-YA

4) **pagtutulúngan** (collaboration)
   pag-tu-tu-LU-ngan

5) **katapátan** (honesty)
   ka-ta-PA-tan

6) **pagtitimpî** (temperance)
   pag-ti-tim-PI

7) **pananagútan** (responsibility)
   pa-na-na-GU-tan

8) **pananampalatáya** (faith)
   pa-na-nam-pa-la-TA-ya

9) **katapángan** (courage)
   ka-ta-PA-ngan

10) **kabaítan** (kindness)
    ka-ba-I-tan

11) **pangáko** (commitment)
    pa-NGA-ko

12) **siglá** (enthusiasm)
    sig-LA

13) **pagtitiwalà** (trust)
    pag-ti-ti-wa-LA

14) **pagigíng maágap** (punctuality)
    pa-gi-GING-ma-A-gap

Ang katapatan ay napakahalaga sa isang mag-asawa.
Honesty is very important in a couple.

Pinagtitiwalaan kita.
I trust you.

Marami akong mga pananagutan sa trabaho.
I have a lot of responsibilities at work.

ANG KATAWAN NG TAO (THE HUMAN BODY)

1) **úlo** (head)
   U-lo

2) **buhók** (hair)
   bu-HOK

3) **mukhâ** (face)
   muk-HA

4) **noó** (forehead)
   no-O

5) **taínga** (ear)
   ta-I-nga

6) **matá** (eyes)
   ma-TA

7) **ilóng** (nose)
   i-LONG

8) **pisngí** (cheek)
   pis-NGI

9) **bibíg** (mouth)
   bi-BIG

10) **bábâ** (chin)
    BA-ba

11) **leég** (neck)
    le-EG

12) **likód** (back)
    li-KOD

13) **dibdíb** (chest)
    dib-DIB

14) **balíkat** (shoulder)
    ba-LI-kat

15) **bráso** (arm)
    BRA-so

16) **bísig** (forearm)
    BI-sig

17) **kamáy** (hand)
    ka-MAY

18) **tiyán** (abdomen)
    ti-YAN

19) **baywáng** (waist)
    bay-WANG

20) **balakáng** (hip)
    ba-la-KANG

21) **bintî** (leg)
    bin-TI

22) **hítâ** (thigh)
    HI-ta

23) **túhod** (knee)
    TU-hod

24) **bintî** (calf)
    bin-TI

25) **lulód** (shin)
    lu-LOD

26) **paá** (foot)
    pa-A

Nabali ang aking braso noong ako ay pitong taon.
I broke my arm when I was seven.

Sumasakit pa rin ba ang iyong likod?
Does your back still hurt?

Sinipa niya ako sa aking binti.
He kicked me in the leg.

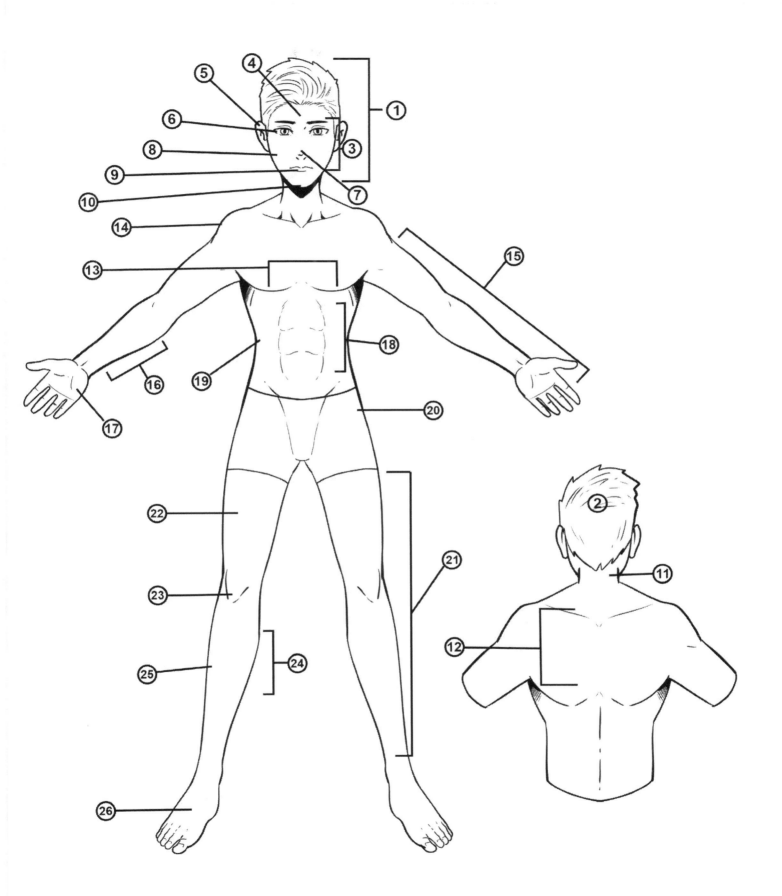

SA LOOB NG KATAWAN NG TAO (INSIDE THE HUMAN BODY)

1) **balát** (skin)
   ba-LAT

2) **kalamnán** (muscles)
   ka-lam-NAN

3) **butó** (bones)
   bu-TO

4) **útak** (brain)
   U-tak

5) **táyroyd** (thyroid)
   TAY-royd

6) **ugát** (vein)
   u-GAT

7) **artérya** (artery)
   ar-TER-ya

8) **púsô** (heart)
   PU-so

9) **bágâ** (lung)
   BA-ga

10) **tiyán** (stomach)
    ti-YAN

11) **esópagó** (esophagus)
    e-SO-pa-GO

12) **lapáy** (pancreas)
    la-PAY

13) **atáy** (liver)
    a-TAY

14) **maliít na bitúka** (small intestine)
    ma-li-IT-na-bi-TU-ka

15) **malakíng bitúka** (large intestine)
    ma-la-KING-bi-TU-ka

16) **apdó** (gallbladder)
    ap-DO

17) **bató** (kidney)
    ba-TO

18) **pantóg** (urinary bladder)
    pan-TOG

Nagkaroon ako ng operasyon sa aking mga bato.
I had an operation on my kidneys.

Masama ang paninigarilyo sa mga baga.
Smoking is bad for the lungs.

Mayroon akong hartbern.
I have heartburn.

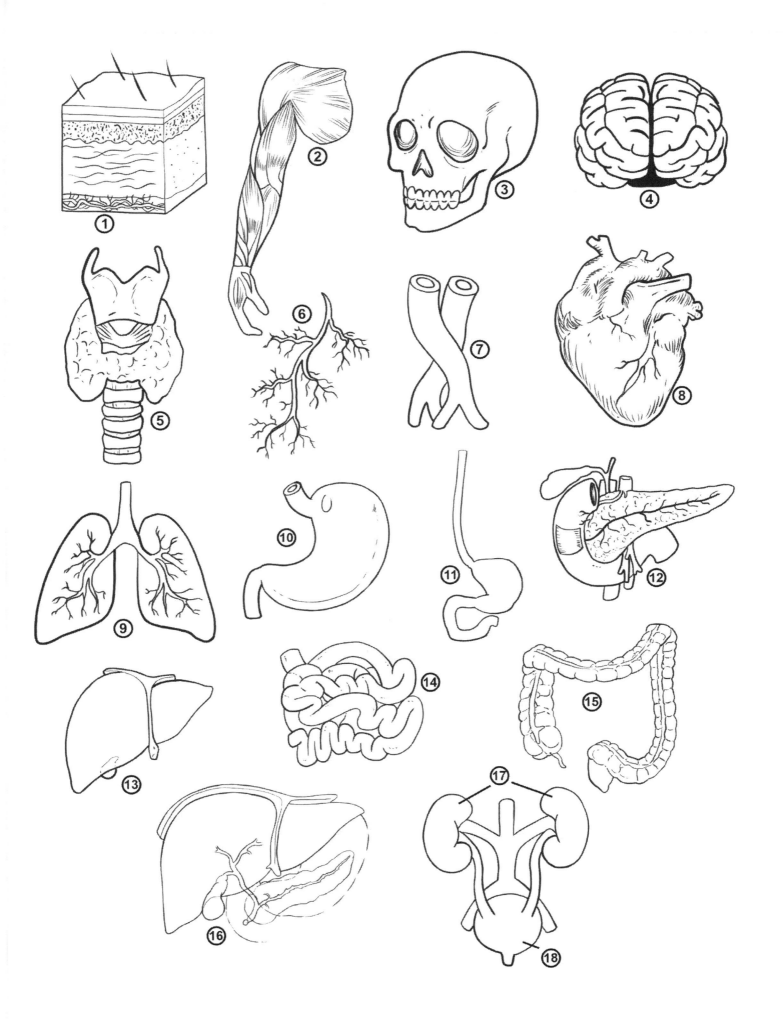

MGA ALAGANG HAYOP (PETS)

1) **áso** (dog)
A-so

2) **púsâ** (cat)
PU-sa

3) **péret** (ferret)
PE-ret

4) **biík** (mini pig/teacup pig/piglet)
bi-IK

5) **kabáyo** (horse)
ka-BA-yo

6) **kulibangbáng** (angelfish)
ku-li-bang-BANG

7) **klawn fis** (clown fish)
KLAWN-FIS

8) **goldfish** (goldfish)
GOLD-fis

9) **dagâng kósta** (hamster)
da-GANG-KOS-ta

10) **konehilyo** (guinea pig)
ko-ne-HIL-yo

11) **dagâ** (mouse)
da-GA

12) **kuného** (rabbit)
ku-NE-ho

13) **parkupíno** (hedgehog)
par-ku-PI-no

14) **tarántúla** (tarantula)
ta-RAN-TU-la

15) **kolónya ng langgám** (ant colony)
ko-LON-ya-ng-lang-GAM

16) **pawíkan** (tortoise)
pa-WI-kan

17) **áhas** (snake)
A-has

18) **hunyangò** (chameleon)
hun-ya-NGO

19) **iguána** (iguana)
ig-WA-na

20) **kanáryo** (canary)
ka-NAR-yo

21) **lóro** (parrot)
LO-ro

22) **muntíng lóro** (parakeet)
mun-TING-LO-ro

Mas gusto ko ang mga aso kaysa sa mga pusa.
I prefer dogs over cats.

Nagregalo ako ng goldfish sa aking anak na babae.
I gifted a goldfish to my daughter.

Dapat nating iligtas ang pawikan.
We must save the tortoise.

ANG HAYUPAN (THE ZOO)

1) **elepánte** (elephant)
e-le-PAN-te

2) **rinóseró** (rhino)
ri-NO-se-RO

3) **dyiráf** (giraffe)
dyi-RAF

4) **sébra** (zebra)
SE-bra

5) **hípopotámo** (hippopotamus)
HI-po-po-TA-mo

6) **tsíte** (cheetah)
TSI-te

7) **tígre** (tiger)
TI-gre

8) **león** (lion)
le-YON

9) **tsímpanse** (chimpanzee)
TSIM-pan-se

10) **oranggután** (orangutan)
o-rang-gu-TAN

11) **babún** (baboon)
ba-BUN

12) **kánggarú** (kangaroo)
KANG-ga-RU

13) **koála** (koala)
ko-WA-la

14) **lémur** (lemur)
LE-mur

Ang leon ay ang hari ng mga hayop.
The lion is the king of animals.

Nag-alaga ako ng isang koala sa Australia.
I petted a koala in Australia.

Ang mga elepante ay napakatalino.
Elephants are very intelligent.

MGA IBON (BIRDS)

1) **abestrús** (ostrich)
   a-bes-TRUS

2) **páboreál** (peacock)
   PA-bo-re-AL

3) **pábo** (turkey)
   PA-bo

4) **tandáng** (rooster)
   tan-DANG

5) **bíbe** (duck)
   BI-be

6) **sísne** (swan)
   SIS-ne

7) **pélikáno** (pelican)
   PE-li-KA-no

8) **plaméngko** (flamingo)
   pla-MENG-ko

9) **kalapáti** (pigeon)
   ka-la-PA-ti

10) **kuwágo** (owl)
    ku-WA-go

11) **buwítre** (vulture)
    bu-WIT-re

12) **ágilá** (eagle)
    A-gi-LA

13) **tagák** (seagull)
    ta-GAK

14) **uwák** (crow)
    u-WAK

15) **tókan** (toucan)
    TO-kan

16) **pénguwin** (penguin)
    PENG-gwin

17) **taríktik** (woodpecker)
    ta-RIK-tik

18) **lóro** (macaw)
    LO-ro

19) **kolúbri** (hummingbird)
    ko-LU-bri

20) **kíwi** (kiwi)
    KI-wi

Ang tandang ay ang simbolo ng Pransiya.
The rooster is the symbol of France.

Nagmamalaki siya tulad ng isang paboreal.
He is proud as a peacock.

Kakain kami ng pabo para sa Pasko.
We are going to eat turkey for Christmas.

QUIZ #1

Use arrows to match the corresponding translations:

a. goldfish

b. leg

c. brother

d. serious

e. flamingo

f. mouse

g. cheetah

h. neighbor

i. cat

j. sad

k. kindness

l. grandson

m. girlfriend

n. curious

o. brain

p. nose

1. malungkot

2. apong lalaki

3. ilong

4. utak

5. kabaitan

6. tsite

7. mausisa

8. pusa

9. plamengko

10. kapatid na lalaki

11. binti

12. daga

13. goldfish

14. kapitbahay

15. seryoso

16. nobya

Fill in the blank spaces with the options below (use each word only once):

Ang aking _____ at ang aking ama ay hindi nagkasama sa loob ng ilang taon. Ang lahat ay laging _____ kung paano silang nagkakasundo para sa_____. Ang aking _____ ay ang aking matalik na kaibigan. Siya ay puno ng _____ at mayroong isang ginintuang_____. Para sa akin, ako ay _____ at ang lahat ay nagsasabi na ako ay puno ng _____. Gustung-gusto ko ang mga hayop, lalo na ang _____. Bukas ng gabi ay inanyayahan kami sa bahay ng ama ko para maghapunan. Palagay ko ay maghahanda siya ng _____. Sana ay gumanda ang pakiramdam ko dahil ngayon ay napakasakit ng aking _____ at _____ ang aking ilong.

nagtataka   kabaitan

katapangan   kapatid na babae

pabo   mga aso

naghiwalay na mag-asawa   barado

puso   ulo

ina   seryoso

MGA REPTILYA AT AMPIBYAN (REPTILES AND AMPHIBIANS)

- **Mga Reptílya (Reptiles)**
  ma-NGA-rep-TIL-ya

1) **anakónda** (anaconda)
   a-na-KON-da

2) **ulupóng** (king cobra)
   u-lu-PONG

3) **rattlesnake** (rattlesnake)
   RA-tel-sneyk

4) **kóral isnéyk** (coral snake)
   KO-ral-is-NEYK

5) **may sungáy na butikî** (horned lizard)
   may-su-NGAY-na-bu-ti-KI

6) **pagárbong leég na butikî** (frill-necked lizard)
   pa-GAR-bong-le-EG-na-bu-ti-KI

7) **karaníwang basilísko** (common basilisk/Jesus Christ lizard)
   ka-ra-NI-wang-ba-si-LIS-ko

8) **Kómodóng dragón** (Komodo dragon)
   KO-mo-DONG- dra-GON

9) **buwáya** (crocodile)
   bu-WA-ya

10) **gáviyal** (gharial/gavial)
    GA-vi-yal

11) **pawíkan** (sea turtle)
    pa-WI-kan

- **Mga Ampibyan (Amphibians)**
  ma-NGA-am-PIB-yan

12) **salamánder** (salamander)
    sa-la-MAN-der

13) **palakâng góliat** (Goliath frog)
    pa-la-KANG-GOL-yat

Ang ilog na ito ay puno ng mga buwaya.
This river is full of crocodiles.

Mayroon akong isang Komodong dragon sa aking vivarium.
I have a Komodo dragon in my vivarium.

Dapat nating protektahan ang mga pawikan mula sa polusyon.
We must protect sea turtles from pollution.

MGA INSEKTO AT ARAKNIDA (INSECTS AND ARACHNIDS)

- **Mga Insékto (Insects)**
  ma-NGA-in-SEK-to

1) **bubúyog** (bee)
   bu-BU-yog

2) **himbubúyog** (bumblebee)
   him-bu-BU-yog

3) **putaktí** (wasp)
   pu-tak-TI

4) **úwang** (beetle)
   U-wang

5) **paruparó** (butterfly)
   pa-ru-pa-RO

6) **gamúgamó (**moth)
   ga-MU-ga-MO

7) **tutubí** (dragonfly)
   tu-tu-BI

8) **ladybug** (ladybug)
   ley-DI-bag

9) **alitaptáp** (firefly)
   a-li-tap-TAP

10) **ípis** (cockroach)
    I-pis

11) **nikník** (horsefly)
    nik-NIK

12) **lángaw** (fly)
    LA-ngaw

13) **lamók** (mosquito)
    la-MOK

14) **tipaklóng** (grasshopper)
    ti-pak-LONG

15) **kuliglíg** (cricket)
    ku-lig-LIG

- **Mga Aráknída (Arachnids)**
  ma-NGA-a-RAK-NI-da

16) **alakdán** (scorpion)
    a-lak-DAN

17) **gagambá** (spider)
    ga-gam-BA

18) **itím na bálo** (Southern black widow)
    i-TIM-na-BA-lo

Ayaw ko sa mga gagamba.
I hate spiders.

Kinagat ako ng isang putakti.
I got stung by a wasp.

Ang mga ladybug ay nagdadala ng suwerte.
Ladybugs bring good luck.

MGA MAMALYA I (MAMMALS I)

1) **paníki** (bat)
pa-NI-ki

2) **plátipús** (platypus)
PLA-ti-PUS

3) **órka** (killer whale/orca)
OR-ka

4) **lúmba-lúmba** (dolphin)
LUM-ba-LUM-ba

5) **kastór** (beaver)
kas-TOR

6) **gráwndhag** (groundhog)
GRAWND-hag

7) **mole** (mole)
MOWL

8) **ardílya** (squirrel)
ar-DIL-ya

9) **wísel** (weasel)
WI-sel

10) **pósum** (possum/opossum)
PO-sum

11) **dagâ** (rat)
da-GA

12) **liyébre** (hare)
li-YEB-re

13) **bádyer** (badger)
BAD-yer

14) **iskángk** (skunk)
is-KANGK

15) **leopárdo** (leopard)
le-yo-PAR-do

Ang mga bampira ay nagiging mga paniki.
Vampires turn into bats.

Mayroong isang pulang ardilya sa puno.
There is a red squirrel in the tree.

Tingnan mo, mayroon siyang daga sa kanyang balikat!
Look, she has a rat on her shoulder!

MGA MAMALYA II (MAMMALS II)

1) **óso** (bear)
O-so

2) **hayína** (hyena)
ha-YI-na

3) **dyákal** (jackal)
DYA-kal

4) **báka** (cow)
BA-ka

5) **tóro** (bull)
TO-ro

6) **sóro** (fox)
SO-ro

7) **kalabáw** (buffalo)
ka-la-BAW

8) **maláking úsa** (elk/moose)
ma-LA-king-U-sa

9) **túpa** (sheep)
TU-pa

10) **kambíng** (goat)
kam-BING

11) **gasél** (gazelle)
ga-SEL

12) **lóbo** (wolf)
LO-bo

13) **unggóy** (monkey)
ung-GOY

14) **laláking túpa** (ram)
la-LA-king-TUpa

15) **ásno** (donkey)
AS-no

Huwag tumakbo sa harap ng isang oso.
Never run in front of a bear.

Si Little Red Riding Hood ay kinain ng isang lobo.
Little Red Riding Hood was eaten by a wolf.

Ang aking baka ay binibigyan ako ng gatas araw-araw.
My cow gives me milk every day.

ISDA AT MGA MOLUSKO (FISH AND MOLLUSKS)

- **Isdâ (Fish)**
  is-DA

1) **butandíng** (whale shark)
   bu-tan-DING

2) **putîng patíng** (white shark)
   pu-TING-pa-TING

3) **bingkúngan** (hammerhead shark)
   bing-KU-ngan

4) **isdáng espáda** (swordfish/marlin)
   is-DANG-es-PA-da

5) **barakúda** (barracuda)
   ba-ra-KU-da

6) **butéte** (pufferfish)
   bu-TE-te

7) **hitò** (catfish)
   hi-TO

8) **piránha** (piranha)
   pi-RAN-ha

9) **isdáng láwin** (flying fish)
   is-DANG-LA-win

10) **malabános** (moray eel)
    ma-la-BA-nos

11) **pági** (manta ray)
    PA-gi

12) **kabáyong-dágat** (seahorse)
    ka-BA-yong-DA-gat

- **Mga Molúsko (Mollusks)**
  Ma-NGA-mo-LUS-ko

13) **pusít** (squid)
    pu-SIT

14) **hibyâ** (cuttlefish)
    hib-YA

15) **pugíta** (octopus)
    pu-GI-ta

16) **talabá** (oyster)
    ta-la-BA

17) **kabíbe** (clam)
    ka-BI-be

18) **karakól** (nautilus)
    ka-ra-KOL

19) **susô** (snail)
    su-SO

20) **lintáng-katí** (slug)
    lin-TANG-ka-TI

Mag-ingat sa mga puting pating.
Beware of the white sharks.

Ayaw kong kumain ng mga talaba.
I hate eating oysters.

Nakahuli ang kapatid kong lalaki ng isang malaking hito.
My brother caught a huge catfish.

KASUOTAN I (CLOTHING I)

1) **kapóte** (raincoat)
ka-PO-te

2) **húdi** (hoodie)
HU-di

3) **dyáket** (jacket)
DYA-ket

4) **maóng** (jeans)
ma-ONG

5) **salawál na bákser** (boxer shorts)
sa-la-WAL-na-BAK-ser

6) **bóta** (boots)
BO-ta

7) **híkaw** (earrings)
HI-kaw

8) **pangginάw** (sweater)
pang-gi-NAW

9) **kuwintás** (necklace)
ku-win-TAS

10) **bra** (bra)
BRA

11) **léging** (leggings)
LE-ging

12) **médyas** (socks)
MED-yas

13) **blúsa/pantáas** (blouse/top)
BLU-sa/pan-TA-as

14) **pulséras** (bracelet)
pul-SE-ras

15) **kórto** (shorts)
KOR-to

16) **pánti** (panty)
PAN-ti

17) **amerikána** (coat)
a-me-ri-KA-na

18) **damít** (dress)
da-MIT

19) **pitakà** (purse)
pi-ta-KA

20) **sandάlyas** (sandals)
san-DAL-yas

Huwag mong kalimutan ang iyong kapote!
Do not forget your raincoat!

Mayroong butas ang aking medyas.
There is a hole in my sock.

Kapag ikaw ay giniginaw, magsuot ka ng pangginaw.
If you are cold, wear a sweater.

KASUOTAN II (CLOTHING II)

1) **sombréro** (hat)
   som-BRE-ro

2) **tuksédo** (tuxedo/smoking)
   tuk-SE-do

3) **buklód-kurbáta** (bow tie)
   buk-LOD-kur-BA-ta

4) **sapátos** (shoes)
   sa-PA-tos

5) **térno** (suit)
   TER-no

6) **kamiséta** (shirt)
   ka-mi-SE-ta

7) **kurbáta** (tie)
   kur-BA-ta

8) **maléta** (briefcase/case)
   ma-LE-ta

9) **mahabàng manggás na blúsa** (long-sleeved blouse)
   ma-ha-BANG-mang-GAS-na-BLU-sa

10) **ispórts bra** (sports bra)
    is-PORTS-bra

11) **pantalón** (trousers/pants)
    pan-ta-LON

12) **sinturón** (belt)
    sin-tu-RON

13) **singsíng** (ring)
    sing-SING

14) **kamiséta** (T-shirt)
    ka-mi-SE-ta

15) **pálda** (skirt)
    PAL-da

16) **bandána** (scarf)
    ban-DA-na

17) **reló** (watch)
    re-LO

18) **kárgong pantalón** (cargo pants)
    KAR-gong-pan-ta-LON

19) **pitakà** (wallet)
    pi-ta-KA

20) **páyong** (umbrella)
    PA-yong

Ang pera ay nasa maleta.
The money is in the briefcase.

Ang araw ay sumisikat kaya dapat kang magsuot ng sumbrero.
The sun is shining, you must wear a hat.

Nawala ang aking relo.
I have lost my watch.

ANG PANAHON (THE WEATHER)

1) **maáraw** (sunny)
   ma-A-raw

2) **maínit** (hot)
   ma-I-nit

3) **bagyóng buhángin** (sandstorm)
   bag-YONG-bu-HA-ngin

4) **maúlap** (cloudy)
   ma-U-lap

5) **maalinsángan** (warm)
   ma-a-lin-SA-ngan

6) **mahámog** (foggy/misty)
   ma-HA-mog

7) **maulán** (rainy)
   ma-u-LAN

8) **malamíg** (cool)
   ma-la-MIG

9) **paták ng ulán** (raindrop)
   pa-TAK-ng-u-LAN

10) **mahalumigmíg** (humid)
    ma-ha-lu-mig-MIG

11) **bagyó** (storm)
    bag-YO

12) **kidlát** (lightning)
    kid-LAT

13) **mahángin** (windy)
    ma-HA-ngin

14) **maniyébe** (snowy)
    ma-ni-YE-be

15) **malamíg** (cold)
    ma-la-MIG

16) **piráso ng niyébe** (snowflake)
    pi-RA-so-nang-ni-YE-be

Napakainit sa Dubai.
It is very hot in Dubai.

Giniginaw ako.
I am cold.

Hindi kami makapunta sa disyerto dahil sa bagyong buhangin.
We cannot go into the desert because of a sandstorm.

ANG MGA PANAHON – TAGSIBOL (THE SEASONS – SPRING)

1) **hardín** (garden)
   har-DIN

2) **pamumulaklák** (blossom)
   pa-mu-mu-lak-LAK

3) **píknik** (picnic)
   PIK-nik

4) **párke** (park)
   PAR-ke

5) **sakáy sa bisikléta** (bike ride)
   sa-KAY-sa-bi-sik-LE-ta

6) **limonáda** (lemonade)
   li-mo-NA-da

7) **garage sale** (garage sale)
   ga-RAJ-seyl

8) **lakbáy** (trip)
   la-lak-BAY

9) **pára magpintá ng mga bató** (to paint rocks)
   PA-ra-mag-pin-TA-nang-ma-NGA-ba-TO

10) **pára magtaním ng iláng mga bulaklák** (to plant some flowers)
    PA-ra-mag-ta-NIM-nang-i-LANG-ma-NGA-bu-lak-LAK

11) **pára magpalipád ng saranggóla** (to fly a kite)
    PA-ra-mag-pa-li-PAD-nang- sa-rang-GO-la

12) **pára dumaló sa isáng bárbikyú party** (to attend a barbecue)
    PA-ra-du-ma-LO-sa-i-SANG-BAR-bi-KYU-PAR-ty

Sa Sabado, mag-pipiknik tayo sa parke.
On Saturday, we are going to have a picnic in the park.

Nangangarap akong maglakbay at bagtasin ang Amerika.
I dream of going on a road trip through America.

Gusto namin ang mga pagsakay sa bisikleta sa Alpes.
We love bike rides in the Alps.

ANG MGA PANAHON – TAG-ARAW (THE SEASONS – SUMMER)

1) **pára magkámping** (to go camping)
   PA-ra-mag-KAM-ping

2) **water park** (water park)
   WA-ter-park

3) **mga gawáin sa labás** (outdoor
   activities)
   ma-NGA-ga-WA-in-sa-la-BAS

4) **pálangúyan** (swimming pool)
   PA-la-NGU-yan

5) **pára lumangóy** (to swim)
   PA-ra-lu-ma-NGOY

6) **pára magíng kayumanggí** (to get
   tanned)
   PA-ra-ma-GING-ka-yu-mang-GI

7) **sanskrín** (sunscreen)
   san-SKRIN

8) **pantabóy sa insékto** (insect repellent)
   pan-ta-BOY-sa-in-SEK-to

9) **lawà** (lake)
   la-WA

10) **tagapagligtás-búhay**
    (lifesaver/lifeguard)
    ta-ga-pag-lig-TAS-BU-hay

11) **kastílyong buhángin** (sandcastle)
    kas-TIL-yong-bu-HA-ngin

12) **pára mag-hiking** (to go on a hike)
    PA-ra-mag-hay-king-nang-ma-ha-BA

Ang Annecy na Lawa ay maganda.
The Annecy Lake is beautiful.

Mahilig akong magpakayumanggi sa dalampasigan.
I love to tan on the beach.

Huwag mong kalimutan ang iyong sunscreen!
Do not forget your sunscreen!

QUIZ #2

Use arrows to match the corresponding translations:

a. horsefly

b. mole

c. king cobra

d. coat

e. socks

f. Komodo dragon

g. tie

h. slug

i. ring

j. snail

k. sunny

l. beetle

m. bat

n. warm

o. necklace

p. butterfly

1. maaraw

2. medyas

3. singsing

4. uwang

5. mole

6. paniki

7. maalinsangan

8. ulupong

9. amerikana

10. niknik

11. kuwintas

12. suso

13. Komodong dragon

14. paruparo

15. kurbata

16. lintang-kati

Fill in the blank spaces with the options below (use each word only once):

Si Phil ay isang guro sa kindergarten. Noong nakaraang linggo, dinala niya ang kaniyang klase para bisitahin ang isang bukirin. Ayon sa ulat ng panahon, magiging maulan ngunit naging _____ at napaka-_____. Nakasuot si Phil ng _____ at _____. Naglalakad siya ng may _____. Sa kasamaang-palad, hindi siya naging komportable sa buong maghapon. Sa pagbisita sa bukid, nakita ng mga bata ang mga baboy, kabayo at _____. Mayroon ding isang bahay-pukyutan na may daan-daang _____. Sa kabilang banda naman, mayroon ding _____ at isa sa kanila ay kinagat si Phil!

maong   bubuyog

sapin sa paa   maaraw

putakti   baka

maalinsangan   amerikana

ANG MGA PANAHON – TAGLAGAS (THE SEASONS – FALL/AUTUMN)

1) **pagbabágo ng mga dáhon** (changing leaves)
   pag-ba-BA-go-nang-ma-NGA-DA-hon

2) **pára kumolékta ng mga dáhon** (to collect leaves)
   PA-ra-ku-mo-LEK-ta-nang-ma-NGA-DA-hon

3) **kalabása** (pumpkin)
   ka-la-BA-sa

4) **pára mag-úkit ng isáng kalabása** (to carve a pumpkin)
   PA-ra-mag-U-kit-nang-i-SANG-ka-la-BA-sa

5) **pamimitás ng mansánas** (apple picking)
   pa-mi-mi-TAS-nang-man-SA-nas

6) **kóstyum pang-halowin** (Halloween costume)
   KOS-tyum-pang-HA-lo-WIN

7) **Hálowín kéndi** (Halloween candy)
   HA-lo-win-KEN-di

8) **mga mabangóng kandilâ** (spiced candles)
   ma-ba-NGONG-ma-NGA-kan-di-LA

9) **hapúnan ng Pasasalámat** (Thanksgiving dinner)
   ha-PU-nan-nang-pa-sa-sa-LA-mat

10) **kúmot na lána** (wool blanket)
    KU-mot-na-LA-na

11) **pára ihawín ang mga marshmálow** (to roast marshmallows)
    PA-ra-i-ha-WIN-ang-ma-NGA-marsh-MA-low

12) **pára palamutián ang bakúran** (to decorate the yard)
    PA-ra-pa-la-mu-ti-AN-ang-ba-KU-ran

Nag-ukit ako ng isang kalabasa para sa Halloween.
I carved a pumpkin for Halloween.

Bumili ako ng mga mabangong kandila para sa Pasko.
I bought spiced candles for Christmas.

Sa Disyembre, sisimulan kong palamutian ang bakuran.
In December, I start to decorate the yard.

ANG MGA PANAHON – TAGLAMIG (THE SEASONS – WINTER)

1) **maínit na tsokoláte** (hot cocoa/hot chocolate)
ma-I-nit-na-tso-ko-LA-te

2) **parágos** (sled)
pa-RA-gos

3) **guwántes** (mittens)
gu-WAN-tes

4) **makapál na dyáket** (puffy jacket)
ma-ka-PAL-na-DYA-ket

5) **sópas** (soup)
SO-pas

6) **dyíndyerbréd** na biskuwít (gingerbread cookies)
DYIN-dyer-BRED-na-bis-KWIT

7) **nagyeyélong bintanà** (frosty window)
nag-ye-YE-long-bin-ta-NA

8) **kóno ng píno** (pinecone)
KO-no-nang-PI-no

9) **iskéyting** (ice skating)
is-KEY-ting

10) **iskí** (ski)
is-KI

11) **ays ringk** (ice rink)
AYS-RINGK

12) **boláng niyébe** (snowball)
bo-LANG-ni-ye-BE

Mahilig akong uminon ng mainit na tsokolate malapit sa apoy.
I love to drink hot chocolate near the fire.

Nagsimula akong mag-iski sa edad na apat.
I started skiing at the age of four.

Handa na ang sopas.
The soup is ready.

ORAS (TIME)

1) **sóna ng óras** (time zone)
SO-na-nang-O-ras

2) **segúndo** (second)
se-GUN-do

3) **minúto** (minute)
mi-NU-to

4) **óras** (hour)
O-ras

5) **áraw** (day)
A-raw

6) **linggó** (week)
ling-GO

7) **dalawáng linggó** (fortnight)
da-la-WANG-ling-GO

8) **buwán** (month)
bu-WAN

9) **taón** (year)
ta-ON

10) **madalíng áraw** (dawn)
ma-da-LING-A-raw

11) **umága** (morning)
u-MA-ga

12) **tanghalì** (noon/midday)
tang-ha-LI

13) **hápon** (afternoon)
HA-pon

14) **takipsílim** (dusk)
ta-kip-SI-lim

15) **gabí** (night)
ga-BI

16) **hátinggabí** (midnight)
HA-ting-ga-BI

17) **pétsa** (date)
PET-sa

18) **kalendáryo** (calendar)
ka-len-DAR-yo

Ang aking anak na babae ay madalas na gumigising sa gabi.
My daughter wakes up often at night.

Kailan ang iyong kaarawan?
When is your birthday?

Hinihintay ka namin ng alas-dose para sa tanghalian.
We are waiting for you at 12 p.m. for lunch.

① ② ③ ④

⑤ TODAY APRIL 10

⑧ MAY 2020

⑥

		2020				
SUN	MON	TUE	WED	THU	FRI	SAT

⑦

SUN	MON	TUE	WED	THU	FRI	SAT
2	3	4	5	6	7	8
9	10	11	12	13	14	15

⑨

2020			
JAN	FEB	MARCH	APRIL
MAY	JUNE	JULY	AUG
SEPT	OCT	NOV	DEC

⑰ MAY 1

⑱ APRIL 2020

SUN	MON	TUE	WED	THU	FRI	SAT

⑩ ⑪ ⑫ ⑬ ⑭ ⑮ ⑯

ANG BAHAY (THE HOUSE)

1) **átik** (attic)
   A-tik

2) **bubóng** (roof)
   bu-BONG

3) **kísamé** (ceiling)
   plah-FON

4) **tsiminéya** (chimney)
   tsi-mi-NE-ya

5) **padér** (wall)
   pa-DER

6) **balkonáhe** (balcony)
   bal-ko-NA-he

7) **beránda** (porch)
   be-RAN-da

8) **bintanà** (window)
   bin-ta-NA

9) **pérsiyána** (shutters)
   PER-si-YA-na

10) **pintô** (door)
    pin-TO

11) **hagdán** (stairs)
    hag-DAN

12) **balústre** (banister)
    ba-LUS-tre

13) **sahíg** (floor)
    sa-HIG

14) **silóng** (basement)
    si-LONG

15) **likód-baháy** (backyard)
    li-KOD-ba-HAY

16) **garáhe** (garage)
    ga-RA-he

17) **daánan ng sasakyán** (driveway)
    da-A-nan-ng-sa-sak-YAN

18) **bákod** (fence/picket fence)
    BA-kod

19) **busón** (mailbox)
    bu-SON

20) **pasílyo** (hallway/corridor)
    pa-SIL-yo

May mga sapot sa kisame.
There are cobwebs on the ceiling.

Ang iyong likod-bahay ay napakaganda.
Your backyard is very beautiful.

Nahulog ako sa hagdan.
I fell down the stairs.

MGA GAMIT SA KUSINA (KITCHEN ITEMS)

1) **kalán** (stove)
   ka-LAN

2) **máykrowéyb óven** (microwave oven)
   MAY-kro-weyb-O-ven

3) **oven toaster** (toaster oven)
   O-ben-TOWS-ter

4) **de-kuryenteng panghalò** (electric mixer)
   de-KUR-yen-teng-pang-ha-LO

5) **blénder** (blender)
   BLEN-der

6) **tústahan ng tinápay** (toaster)
   TUS-ta-han-ng-ti-NA-pay

7) **coffee maker** (coffee maker)
   ko-PI-mey-ker

8) **pridyider** (fridge)
   PRI-dyi-der

9) **páminggálan** (pantry)
   PA-ming-GA-lan

10) **platéra** (cupboard)
    pla-TE-ra

11) **keyk pan** (cake pan)
    KEYK-pan

12) **kawalì** (frying pan)
    ka-wa-LI

13) **kaldéro** (pot)
    kal-DE-ro

14) **mga panghiwà ng kúkis** (cookie cutters)
    ma-NGA-pang-hi-WA-nang-KU-kis

15) **mangkók sa paghahalò** (mixing bowl)
    mang-KOK-sa-pag-ha-ha-LO

16) **koladór** (colander)
    ko-la-DOR

17) **salaán** (strainer)
    sa-la-AN

18) **pambiló** (rolling pin)
    pam-bi-LO

19) **guwántes pang hurnó** (oven mitt)
    gu-WAN-tes-pang-hur-NO

20) **éypron** (apron)
    EY-pron

Gumamit ako ng blender para gumawa ng isang smoothie.
I used a blender to make a smoothie.

Kumuha ka ng yogurt sa pridyider.
Go get a yogurt in the fridge.

Nirolyo ko ang pastelerya gamit ang isang pambilo.
I rolled the pastry with a rolling pin.

MGA GAMIT SA SILID-TULUGAN (BEDROOM ITEMS)

1) **káma** (bed)
KA-ma

2) **kutsón** (mattress)
kut-SON

3) **kúbre-káma** (bedding/bed linen)
KU-bre-KA-ma

4) **únan** (pillow)
U-nan

5) **sapín** (sheets)
sa-PIN

6) **kúmot** (blanket)
KU-mot

7) **takíp** (spread)
ta-KIP

8) **pundá** (pillowcase)
pun-DA

9) **mésa sa tabí ng kamá** (nightstand)
ME-sa-sa-ta-BI-nang-ka-MA

10) **orasáng pang- mésa** (table clock)
o-ra-SANG-pang-ME-sa

11) **ílaw pang-mésa** (table light)
I-law-sa-Me-sa

12) **aparadór** (closet)
a-pa-ra-DOR

13) **túmba-túmba** (rocking chair)
TUM-ba-TUM-ba

14) **lámpará** (lamp)
LAM-pa-RA

15) **salamín** (mirror)
sa-la-MIN

16) **tokadór** (dresser)
to-ka-DOR

17) **kurtína** (curtain)
kur-TI-na

18) **kúna** (cradle/crib)
KU-na

19) **móbayl sa kúna** (crib mobile)
MO-bayl-sa-KU-na

20) **hanger** (hanger)
HA-nger

Papalitan ko ang mga sapin ng kama.
I am going to change the bedsheets.

Ang sanggol ay nasa kanyang kuna.
The baby is in his crib.

Ang kutsong ito ay napakatigas para sa akin.
This mattress is too hard for me.

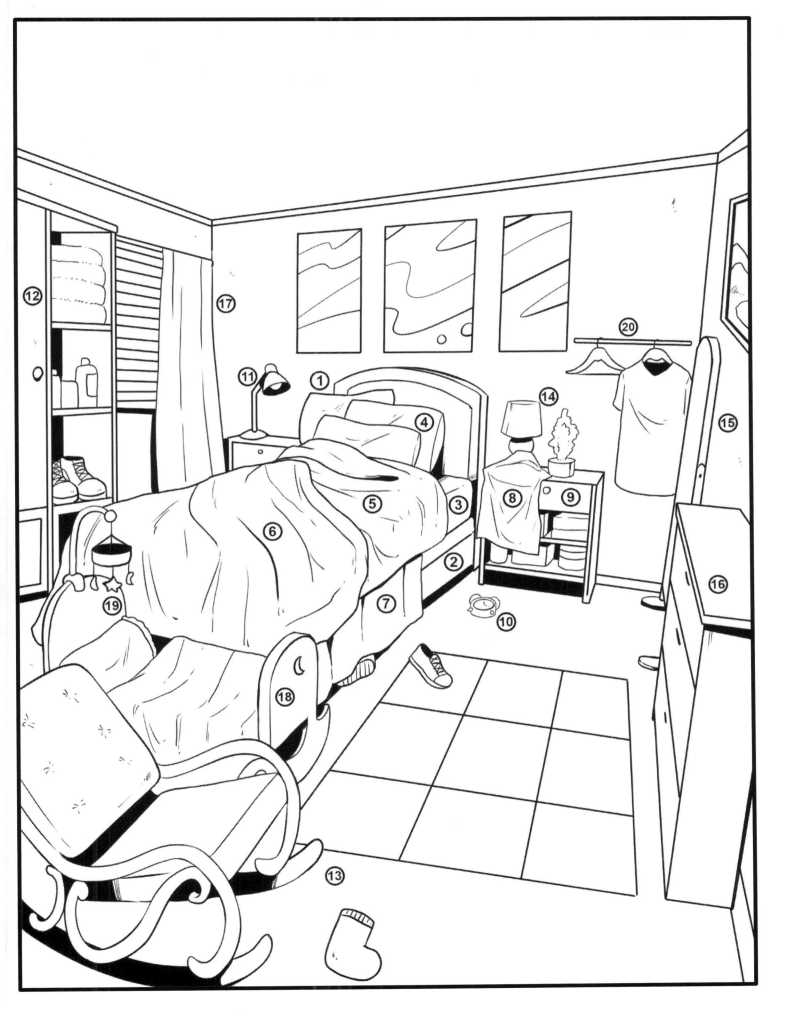

MGA GAMIT SA BANYO (BATHROOM ITEMS)

1) **kúrtinang pampáliguán** (shower curtain)
   KUR-ti-nang-pam-PA-li-gu-AN

2) **tuwálya** (towel)
   tu-WAL-ya

3) **sabitán ng tuwálya** (towel rack)
   sa-bi-TAN-nang-tu-WAL-ya

4) **bímpo** (hand towel)
   BIM-po

5) **banyéra** (bathtub)
   ban-YE-ra

6) **páligúan** (shower)
   PA-li-GU-an

7) **pálikúran/kubéta** (toilet/WC)
   PA-li-KU-ran/ku-BE-ta

8) **labábo** (sink/washbasin)
   la-BA-bo

9) **grípo** (faucet/tap)
   GRI-po

10) **pamalísan** (bathmat)
    pa-ma-LI-san

11) **kábinét ng gamót** (medicine cabinet)
    KA-bi-NET-nang-ga-MOT

12) **tútpeyst** (toothpaste)
    TUT-peyst

13) **sipílyo** (toothbrush)
    si-PIL-yo

14) **syámpu** (shampoo)
    SYAM-pu

15) **sukláy** (comb)
    suk-LAY

16) **sabón** (soap)
    sa-BON

17) **fowm sa pag-áhit** (shaving foam)
    FOWM-sa-pag-A-hit

18) **labáha** (razor/shaver)
    la-BA-ha

19) **tísyu** (toilet paper)
    TIS-yu

20) **pambómba sa kubéta** (plunger)
    pam-BOM-ba-sa-ku-BE-ta

21) **eskóba pang-kubéta** (toilet brush)
    es-KO-ba-pang-ku-BE-ta

22) **básurahán** (wastebasket)
    BA-su-ra-HAN

Wala nang tisyu!
There is no more toilet paper!

Ilagay ang tuwalya sa sabitan.
Place the towel on the towel rack.

Huwag kalimutang isara ang gripo.
Do not forget to turn off the tap.

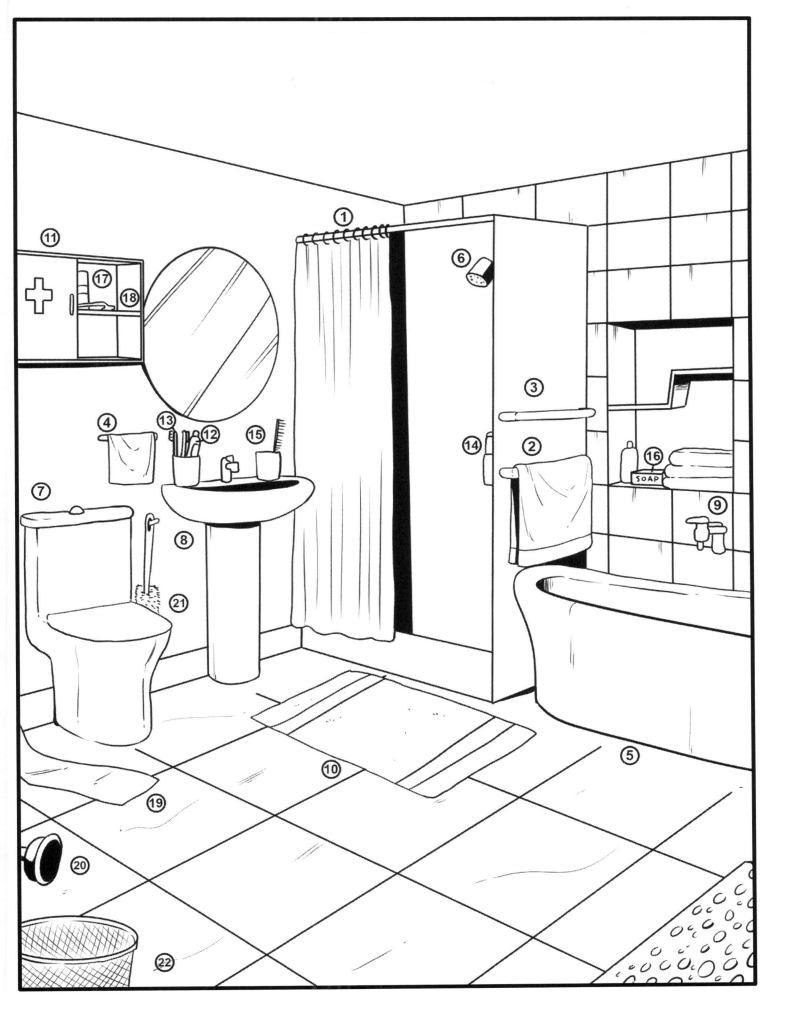

MGA GAMIT SA SALA (LIVING ROOM ITEMS)

1) **múwebles** (furniture)
MU-web-les

2) **sílya** (chair)
SIL-ya

3) **sopá** (sofa)
so-PA

4) **sopá** (couch)
so-PA

5) **kutsón** (cushion)
kut-SON

6) **lamesíta** (coffee table)
la-me-SI-ta

7) **seniséra** (ashtray)
se-ni-SE-ra

8) **ploréra** (vase)
plo-RE-ra

9) **palamutì** (ornaments)
pa-la-mu-TI

10) **estánte** (bookshelf/bookcase)
es-TAN-te

11) **éstante ng mágasín** (magazine holder)
ES-tan-te-nang-MA-ga-SIN

12) **istéryo** (stereo)
is-TER-yo

13) **ispíker** (speakers)
is-PI-ker

14) **apúyan** (fireplace)
a-PU-yan

15) **aránya** (chandelier)
a-RAN-ya

16) **lámpará** (lamp)
LAM-pa-RA

17) **bombílya** (light bulb)
bom-BIL-ya

18) **orasáng pandingdíng** (wall clock)
o-ra-SANG-pan-ding-DING

19) **péynting** (painting)
PEYN-ting

20) **télebisyón** (TV/television)
TE-le-bis-YON

21) **rimówt kontról** (remote control)
ri-MOWT-kon-TROL

22) **console ng video game** (video game console)
KON-sowl-nang-BID-jo-GEYM

Gumugol ako ng maraming oras sa harap ng telebisyon.
I spend too much time in front of the TV.

Ibinili ko ang aking asawa ng isang console ng video game para sa Pasko.
I bought my husband a video game console for Christmas.

Halos natapos ko na ang aking unang peynting.
I have nearly finished my first painting.

MGA GAMIT SA SILID-KAINAN (DINING ROOM ITEMS)

1) **hapág-kainán** (dining table)
   ha-PAG-ka-i-NAN

2) **mantél** (tablecloth)
   man-TEL

3) **centerpiece** (centerpiece)
   SEN-ter-PIS

4) **pléysmat** (placemat)
   PLEYS-mat

5) **pinggán** (plate)
   ping-GAN

6) **serbilyéta** (napkin)
   ser-bil-YE-ta

7) **kutsílyo** (knife)
   kut-SIL-yo

8) **tinidór** (fork)
   ti-ni-DOR

9) **kutsára** (spoon)
   kut-SA-ra

10) **pitsél** (pitcher/jar)
    pit-SEL

11) **báso** (glass)
    BA-so

12) **tása** (mug/cup)
    TA-sa

13) **lalagyán ng asín** (saltshaker)
    la-lag-YAN-nang-a-SIN

14) **lalagyán ng pamintá** (pepper shaker)
    la-lag-YAN-nang-pa-min-TA

15) **bandehádo** (tray)
    ban-de-HA-do

16) **inúmin** (drink/beverage)
    i-NU-min

17) **pagkáin** (food)
    pag-KA-in

18) **meryénda** (snack)
    mer-YEN-da

Dadalhin ko ang iyong almusal na nakalagay sa bandehado.
I will bring you breakfast on a tray.

Aling centerpiece ang iyong pinili para sa iyong kasal?
Which centerpiece have you chosen for your wedding?

Gusto mo ba ng inumin?
Do you want a drink?

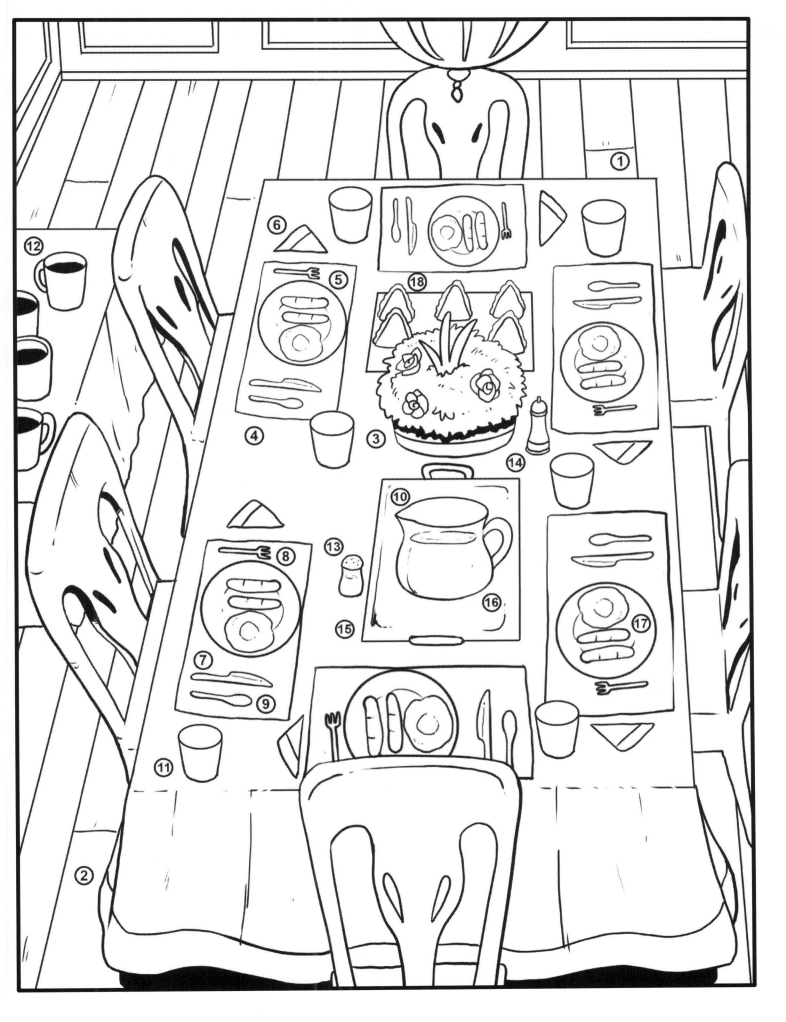

QUIZ #3

Use arrows to match the corresponding translations:

a. morning   1. bintana

b. pumpkin   2. aparador

c. door   3. paragos

d. Halloween costume   4. pader

e. pillow   5. éypron

f. afternoon   6. bolang niyebe

g. sled   7. unan

h. apron   8. kóstyum pang-Hálowín

i. ice rink   9. pinto

j. towel rack   10. tústahan ng tinápay

k. wall   11. hapon

l. closet   12. sabitán ng tuwálya

m. window   13. ice rink

n. fireplace   14. kalabasa

o. snowball   15. apuyan

p. toaster   16. umaga

Fill in the blank spaces with the options below (use each word only once):

Taglagas ang paborito kong panahon. Taun-taon, inaasahan ko ang Oktubre para _____ at gayundin _____. Ako at ang aking pamilya ay gustong-gusto ang _____ at inilalagay ang mga ito sa buong bahay. Lagi kong inilalagay ang isa sa harap ng _____. Nagmumukha ang mga itong maliliit at nakakatakot na mga _____. Ang Oktubre 31 ay Halowin. Naglilibot kami para makakuha ng kendi mula sa mga kapitbahay. Pagkatapos niyon, sa pagsapit ng _____, nagpapa-ilaw kami ng _____at nagre-relaks sa _____ habangumiinom ng _____. Naglalaro naman ang kapatid kong lalaki ng _____. Tuwing Nobyembre, uso ang _____ at pumunta para mag-iskeyting sa _____. Gustung-gusto ko ito!

balkonahe   paghuhukay ng kalabasa

mainit na tsokolate   sopa

hatinggabi   para palamutian ang bakuran

ilawan   mag-iski

mga mabangong kandila   ice rink

video game   tsimineya

ANG HARDIN (THE GARDEN/THE BACKYARD)

1) **hardinéro** (gardener)
   har-di-NE-ro

2) **kamálig** (shed)
   ka-MA-lig

3) **palumpóng** (bush)
   pa-lum-PONG

4) **damuhán** (lawn)
   da-mu-HAN

5) **damó** (grass)
   da-MO

6) **bulaklák** (flower)
   bu-lak-LAK

7) **hos** (garden hose)
   hos

8) **pandilíg** (watering can)
   pan-di-LIG

9) **pasô** (flowerpot)
   pa-SO

10) **guwántes páng-hardín** (gardening gloves)
    gu-WAN-tes-sa-PANG-har-DIN

11) **pála** (shovel)
    PA-la

12) **kalaykáy** (rake)
    ka-lay-KAY

13) **piruyà** (gardening fork)
    pi-ru-YA

14) **gúnting panghaláman** (pruners/pruning shears)
    GUN-ting-pang-ha-LA-man

15) **dulós** (garden trowel)
    du-LOS

16) **grípo** (tap)
    GRI-po

17) **kartílya** (wheelbarrow)
    kar-TIL-ya

18) **pantábas ng damó** (lawn mower)
    pan-TA-bas-nang-da-MO

19) **ilawán** (lantern)
    i-la-WAN

20) **báging** (vine)
    BA-ging

Ang isang baging ay lumalaki sa aking hardin.
A vine grows in my garden.

Inilagay ko ang lahat ng aking mga kagamitan sa kamalig.
I have put all my tools in the shed.

Ang kartilya ay puno ng mga tuyong dahon.
The wheelbarrow is full of dead leaves.

ANG SILID LABAHAN (THE CLEANING ROOM)

1) **mákináng panlabá** (washing machine)
MA-ki-NANG-pan-la-BA

2) **pátuyùan** (dryer)
PA-tu-YU-an

3) **plántsa** (iron)
PLAN-tsa

4) **plantsahán** (ironing board)
PLAN-tsa-HAN

5) **sabóng panlabá** (laundry soap)
sa-BONG-pan-la-BA

6) **panlínis ng labáda** (laundry detergent)
pan-LI-nis-nang-la-BA-da

7) **pampalambót ng téla** (fabric softener)
pam-pa-lam-BOT-nang-TE-la

8) **básket ng labáda** (laundry basket)
BAS-ket-nang-la-BA-da

9) **madumíng damít** (dirty clothes)
ma-du-MING-da-MIT

10) **malínis na labáda** (clean laundry)
ma-LI-nis-na-la-BA-da

11) **walís** (broom)
wa-LIS

12) **dáspan** (dust pan)
DAS-pan

13) **gómang guwántes** (rubber gloves)
GO-mang-gu-WAN-tes

14) **espóngha** (sponge)
es-PONG-ha

15) **plástik na palanggána** (plastic tub)
PLAS-tik-na-pa-lang-GA-na

16) **panlampáso** (mop)
pan-lam-PA-so

17) **timbâ** (bucket)
tim-BA

18) **pamúnas** (cleaning cloths)
pa-MU-nas

19) **eskóba** (scrub brush)
es-KO-ba

20) **pampaputî** (bleach)
pam-pa-pu-TI

21) **pandesimpektá** (disinfectant)
pan-des-im-pek-TA

22) **básurahán** (garbage can)
BA-su-ra-HAN

Hindi ko gusto ang paglalaba.
I hate doing the laundry.

Dapat mong lampasuhin ang sahig.
You must mop the floor.

Maaari kang gumamit ng pampalambot ng tela sa makinang panlaba.
You can use fabric softener in the washing machine.

ANG PAARALAN / ANG PAMANTASAN (THE SCHOOL/THE UNIVERSITY)

1) **gurô** (teacher)
gu-RO

2) **mág-aarál** (student)
MAG-a-a-RAL

3) **silíd-arálan** (classroom)
si-LID-a-RA-lan

4) **aparadór** (locker)
a-pa-ra-DOR

5) **paskílan** (bulletin board)
pas-KI-lan

6) **pirásong papél** (sheet of paper)
pi-RA-song-pa-PEL

7) **aklát** (book)
ak-LAT

8) **kuwadérno** (notebook)
ku-wa-DER-no

9) **pandikít** (glue)
pan-di-KIT

10) **guntíng** (scissors)
gun-TING

11) **lapís** (pencil)
la-PIS

12) **pamburá** (eraser)
pam-bu-RA

13) **pantasá** (pencil sharpener)
pan-ta-SA

14) **panúlat** (pen)
pa-NU-lat

15) **panandâ** (marker)
pa-nan-DA

16) **pangmarká** (highlighter)
pang-mar-KA

17) **sóbre** (envelope)
SO-bre

18) **klipbórd** (clipboard)
klip-BORD

19) **pisára** (blackboard)
pi-sa-RA

20) **kalkuladór** (calculator)
kal-ku-la-DOR

21) **rúler** (ruler)
RU-ler

22) **istéypler** (stapler)
is-TEYP-ler

23) **lalagyán ng lápis** (pouch/pencil case)
la-lag-YAN-nang-LA-pis

24) **mésa** (school desk)
ME-sa

25) **lamésa** (table)
la-ME-sa

26) **láptap** (laptop)
LAP-tap

Ang kalkulasyon ay sobrang komplikadong wala ang kalkulador.
This calculation is too complicated without a calculator.

Gamitin ang iyong pambura para itama ang iyong pagkakamali.
Use your eraser to correct your mistake.

Hindi ko makita ang aking pantasa.
I cannot find my pencil sharpener.

ANG OPISINA (THE OFFICE)

1) **ámo** (boss)
A-mo

2) **superyór** (superior)
su-per-YOR

3) **kawaní** (employee)
ka-wa-NI

4) **pangúlo** (CEO/president)
pa-NGU-lo

5) **kasósyo sa negósyo** (business partner)
ka-SOS-yo-sa-ne-GOS-yo

6) **kasamahán** (colleague)
ka-sa-ma-HAN

7) **katrábaho** (co-worker)
ka-TRA-ba-ho

8) **kalíhim** (secretary)
ka-LI-him

9) **maliít na silíd** (cubicle)
ma-li-IT-na-si-LID

10) **swivel chair** (swivel chair)
SWI-bel-CHEYR

11) **mésa** (desk)
ME-sa

12) **kompyúter** (computer)
kom-PYU-ter

13) **prínter** (printer)
PRIN-ter

14) **mga supláy sa opisína** (office supplies)
ma-nga-sup-LAY-sa-o-pi-SI-na

15) **gománg pantaták** (rubber stamp)
GO-mang-pan-ta-TAK

16) **dispenséro ng teyp** (tape dispenser)
dis-pen-SE-ro-nang-TEYP

17) **pólder** (folder)
POL-der

18) **fáyling kábinét** (filing cabinet)
FAY-ling-KA-bi-NET

19) **fax** (fax)
FAX

20) **teléponó** (telephone)
te-LE-po-NO

Gusto ko talaga ang aking bagong kasamahan.
I really like my new colleague.

Ibigay mo ang iyong numero sa aking kalihim.
Give your number to my secretary.

Wala nang gumagamit ng fax!
No one uses a fax anymore!

MGA HANAPBUHAY (PROFESSIONS/OCCUPATIONS)

1) **inhenyéro** (engineer)
   in-hen-YE-ro

2) **ástronót** (astronaut)
   AS-tro-NOT

3) **pilóto** (pilot)
   pi-LO-to

4) **hukóm** (judge)
   hu-KOM

5) **bumbéro** (firefighter)
   bum-BE-ro

6) **pulís** (police officer)
   pu-LIS

7) **tagalúto** (chef)
   ta-ga-LU-to

8) **konduktór** (conductor)
   kon-duk-TOR

9) **propesór** (professor)
   pro-pe-SOR

10) **mananáyaw** (dancer)
    ma-na-NA-yaw

11) **negósyánte** (businessman)
    ne-GOS-YAN-te

12) **tagasánay ng háyop** (animal trainer)
    ta-ga-SA-nay-nang-HA-yop

Noong ako ay bata pa, gusto kong maging isang piloto.
When I was a kid, I wanted to be a pilot.

Siya ay magiging isang magaling na negosyante.
He will become a good businessman.

Tawagin ang mga bumbero!
Call the firefighters!

MGA PARAAN NG TRANSPORTASYON (MEANS OF TRANSPORT)

1) **bisikléta** (bike/bicycle)
   bi-sik-LE-ta

2) **motorsíklo** (motorcycle/motorbike)
   mo-tor-SIK-lo

3) **isnówmóbayl** (snowmobile)
   is-NOW-MO-bayl

4) **kótse** (car/automobile)
   KOT-se

5) **bus** (bus)
   BUS

6) **trak** (truck)
   TRAK

7) **sábwey** (subway)
   SAB-wey

8) **tren** (train)
   TREN

9) **jet iskí** (jet ski)
   JET-is-KI

10) **bangkâ** (boat)
    bang-KA

11) **barkóng panlayág** (cruise ship)
    bar-KONG-pan-la-YAG

12) **submaríno** (submarine)
    sub-ma-RI-no

13) **sepelín** (blimp/Zeppelin)
    se-pe-LIN

14) **hot air balloon** (hot-air balloon)
    HAT-EYR-ba-LUN

15) **eropláno** (plane/airplane)
    e-ro-PLA-no

16) **helikópter** (helicopter/chopper)
    he-li-KOP-ter

17) **sasakyáng pangkalawákan** (space shuttle)
    sa-sak-YANG-pang-ka-la-WA-kan

Sasakay ka ba sa bus o sa iyong kotse?
Are you going to take the bus or your car?

Takot ako sa paglipad.
I am scared of flying.

Nai-book namin ang bakasyon sa isang barkong panlayag.
We have booked a holiday on a cruise ship.

MGA TANAWIN (LANDSCAPES)

1) **bundók** (mountain)
   bun-DOK

2) **trópikong kagubátan** (tropical rainforest)
   TRO-pi-kong-ka-gu-BA-tan

3) **disyérto** (desert)
   dis-YER-to

4) **bulkán** (volcano)
   vol-CAN

5) **bangín** (cliff)
   ba-NGIN

6) **dalampasígan** (beach)
   da-lam-pa-SI-gan

7) **gubát** (forest)
   gu-BAT

8) **kuwéba** (cave)
   ku-WE-ba

9) **géyser** (geyser)
   GEY-ser

10) **talón** (waterfall/falls)
    ta-LON

11) **ílog** (river)
    I-log

12) **sinaúnang mga guhò** (ancient ruins)
    si-na-U-nang-ma-nga-gu-HO

Naligaw ako sa gubat.
I got lost in the forest.

Ang pinakamagagandang bakasyon ay ginugugol sa mga bundok.
The best holidays are spent in the mountains.

Dapat tayong tumawid sa ilog.
We must cross the river.

MGA PALAKASAN I (SPORTS I)

1) **pamamaná** (archery)
   pa-ma-ma-NA

2) **bóksing** (boxing)
   BOK-sing

3) **pagbibisikléta** (cycling)
   pag-bi-bi-sik-LE-ta

4) **eskríma** (fencing)
   es-KRI-ma

5) **fútbol** (football/soccer)
   FUT-bol

6) **rágbi** (rugby)
   RAG-bi

7) **píngpong** (table tennis/ping pong)
   PING-pong

8) **báliból** (volleyball)
   BA-li-BOL

9) **pagbabárbel** (weightlift)
   pagba-BAR-bel

10) **iskéyting** (skating)
    is-KEY-ting

11) **paralímpikong pálakásan**
    (paralympic sports)
    pa-ra-LIM-pi-kong-PA-la-KA-san

12) **béysbol** (baseball)
    BEYS-bol

13) **básketból** (basketball)
    BAS-ket-BOL

Hinahangaan ko talaga ang ragbi na mga manlalaro.
I really admire rugby players.

Pumupunta ako sa gym para gawin ang pagbabarbel.
I go to the gym to do weightlifting.

Gusto ng mga Pilipino ang pagbibisikleta.
Filipino people love cycling.

MGA PALAKASAN II (SPORTS II)

1) **bádmintón** (badminton)
   BAD-min-TON

2) **himnástikó** (gymnastics)
   him-NAS-ti-KO

3) **paggáod** (rowing)
   pag-GA-od

4) **pag-akyát na pálakásan** (sport climbing)
   pag-ak-YAT-sa-PA-la-KA-san

5) **surfing** (surfing)
   SER-fing

6) **ténis** (tennis)
   TE-nis

7) **trámpolína** (trampoline)
   TRAM-po-LI-na

8) **págbubunô** (wrestling)
   PAG-bu-bu-NO

9) **pag-iiskí** (skiing)
   pag-i-is-KI

10) **iskéletón** (skeleton)
    is-KE-le-TON

11) **pigúrang iskéyting** (figure skating)
    pi-GU-rang-is-KEY-ting

12) **paglangóy** (swimming)
    pag-la-NGOY

13) **pólong pantúbig** (water polo)
    PO-long-pan-TU-big

14) **hakí** (hockey)
    ha-KI

Ang paggaod ay napakapopular sa Inglatera.
Rowing is very popular in England.

Si Serena Williams ay ang pinakamagaling na manlalaro ng tenis.
Serena Williams is the best tennis player.

Hindi ko alam ang mga tuntunin ng polong pantubig.
I do not know the rules of water polo.

ARAW NG PASKO (CHRISTMAS DAY)

1) **ligás** (mistletoe)
   li-GAS

2) **gárland** (garland)
   GAR-land

3) **punòng Pampaskó** (Christmas tree)
   pu-NONG-pam-pas-KO

4) **dekorasyóng Pampaskó** (Christmas decorations)
   de-ko-ras-YONG-pam-pas-KO

5) **regálong Pamaskó** (Christmas gifts/presents)
   re-GA-long- pa-mas-KO

6) **Pampaskóng hapúnan** (Christmas dinner)
   pam-pas-KONG-ha-PU-nan

7) **kénding bastón** (candy cane)
   KEN-ding-bas-TON

8) **húgis laláking dyíndyerbréd** (gingerbread man)
   HU-gis-la-LA-king-DYIN-dyer-BRED

9) **duwénde ng Paskó** (Christmas elf)
   du-WEN-de-nang-pas-KO

10) **sombrérong Pamaskó** (Christmas hat)
    som-BRE-rong-pa-mas-KO

11) **Sánta Klaws** (Santa Claus)
    SAN-ta-KLAWS

12) **parágos ni Sánta** (Santa's sleigh)
    pa-RA-gos-ni-SAN-ta

13) **bituín ng Paskó** (Christmas star)
    bi-tu-IN-nang-pas-KO

14) **isnówman** (snowman)
    is-NOW-man

15) **kandílâ** (candles)
    kan-DI-la

Kakain kami ng salmon para sa Pampaskong hapunan.
We will eat salmon for Christmas dinner.

Si Santa Klaws ay pumapasok sa pamamagitan ng tsimeneya.
Santa Claus enters through the chimney.

Bumili ako ng isang artipisyal na punong Pampasko.
I bought an artificial Christmas tree.

95

QUIZ #4

Use arrows to match the corresponding translations:

a. engineer

b. printer

c. wheelbarrow

d. mop

e. colleague

f. gardener

g. bike

h. cave

i. plane

j. calculator

k. firefighter

l. boat

m. dirty laundry

n. washing machine

o. rake

p. classroom

1. bumbero

2. kalkulador

3. silid-aralan

4. maruming labada

5. makinang panlaba

6. kalaykay

7. printer

8. eroplano

9. kartilya

10. hardinero

11. kasamahan

12. bisikleta

13. panlampaso

14. kuweba

15. inhinyero

16. bangka

Fill in the blank spaces with the options below (use each word only once):

Si Gérald ay _____ ng inhinyerong sibil sa Unibersidad ng Nantes. Siya ay nasa kanyang ikatlong taon. Kalaunan, gusto niyang maging _____ o_____. Ang kanyang mithiin ay maging mayaman at maglakbay sa mundo. Nangangarap siyang maglaro ng _____ sa isang _____ sa Caribbean, bibili ng kanyang sariling _____o mag-_____ sa dagat. Ang paborito niyang _____ ay si G. Rendal. Siya ay napakatalino at karismatiko. Umaasa si Gerald na maging katulad niya kalaunan. Ngunit sa ngayon, kailangan niyang pumunta sa laundromat para gamitin ang _____ at labhan ang kanyang _____. Bago iyon, kailangan niyang pumunta sa pamilihan para bumili ng _____ at _____ dahil wala na siya ng mga ito.

propesor	maruming labada
panlaba	inhinyero
balibol	jet ski
dalampasigan	makinang panlaba
pampalambot ng tela	mag-aaral
negosyante	bangka

MGA INSTRUMENTO SA MUSIKA (MUSICAL INSTRUMENTS)

1) **gitára** (acoustic guitar)
gi-TA-ra

2) **gitárang de koryénte** (electric guitar)
gi-TA-rang-de-kor-YEN-te

3) **gitárang báho** (bass guitar)
gi-TA-rang-BA-ho

4) **tamból** (drum)
tam-BOL

5) **piyáno** (piano)
pi-YA-no

6) **trumpéta** (trumpet)
trum-PE-ta

7) **silíndro** (harmonica)
si-LIN-dro

8) **pláwta** (flute)
PLAW-ta

9) **klarinéte** (clarinet)
kla-ri-NE-te

10) **álpa** (harp)
AL-pa

11) **bágpayp** (bagpipes)
BAG-payp

12) **tsélo** (cello)
TSE-lo

13) **biyolín** (violin)
bi-yo-LIN

14) **saksópon** (saxophone)
sak-SO-pon

Nagsimula na akong mag-aral tumugtog ng piyano.
I have started taking piano lessons.

Ang alpa ang aking paboritong instrumento.
The harp is my favorite instrument.

Si Jimmy Hendrix ay naging isang henyo sa gitara.
Jimmy Hendrix was a guitar genius.

MGA PRUTAS (FRUITS)

1) **présas** (strawberry)
   PRE-sas

2) **papáya** (papaya)
   pa-PA-ya

3) **sinigwélas** (plum)
   si-nig-WE-las

4) **milón** (melon)
   mi-LON

5) **pakwán** (watermelon)
   pak-WAN

6) **ságing** (banana)
   SA-ging

7) **manggá** (mango)
   mang-GA

8) **melokotón** (peach)
   me-lo-ko-TON

9) **rasbéri** (raspberry)
   ras-BE-ri

10) **kahél** (orange)
    ka-HEL

11) **limón** (lemon)
    li-MON

12) **pinyá** (pineapple)
    pin-YA

13) **dáyap** (lime)
    DA-yap

14) **úbas** (grapes)
    U-bas

15) **serésa** (cherry)
    se-RE-sa

16) **mansánas** (apple)
    man-SA-nas

17) **péras** (pear)
    PE-ras

18) **suhâ** (grapefruit)
    su-HA

19) **guyabáno** (soursop)
    gu-ya-BA-no

20) **niyóg** (coconut)
    ni-YOG

Gusto ko ang isang kilo ng mga peras.
I would like a kilo of pears.

Kumakain siya ng suha sa almusal.
He eats a grapefruit for breakfast.

Gusto ko ang minatamis na rasberi .
I love raspberry jam.

MGA GULAY (VEGETABLES)

1) **kóliplór** (cauliflower)
KO-lip-LOR

2) **aspáragó** (asparagus)
as-PA-ra-GO

3) **brókoli** (broccoli)
BRO-ko-li

4) **repólyo** (cabbage)
re-POL-yo

5) **alkatsópas** (artichoke)
al-ka-TSO-pas

6) **usbóng ng Brúselas** (Brussels sprout)
us-BONG-nang-BRU-se-las

7) **maís** (corn)
ma-IS

8) **litsúgas** (lettuce)
li-TSU-gas

9) **éspináka** (spinach)
ES-pi-na-ka

10) **kamátis** (tomato)
ka-MA-tis

11) **pipíno** (cucumber)
pi-PI-no

12) **zucchini** (zucchini)
ZU-ki-ni

13) **kabuté** (mushroom)
ka-bu-TE

14) **arúgula** (arugula)
a-RU-gu-la

15) **talóng** (eggplant)
ta-LONG

16) **atsál** (bell pepper)
at-SAL

17) **sibúyas** (onion)
si-BU-yas

18) **kalabása** (pumpkin/squash)
ka-la-BA-sa

19) **patátas** (potato)
pa-TA-tas

20) **Swiss chard** (Swiss chard)
SWISS-CHARD

Naghanda ako ng isang sopas na gawa sa repolyo.
I prepared cabbage soup.

Kulang ng sarsa ang salad na kamatis.
The tomato salad lacks sauce.

Mayroong mga talong sa Moussaka.
There are eggplants in the Moussaka.

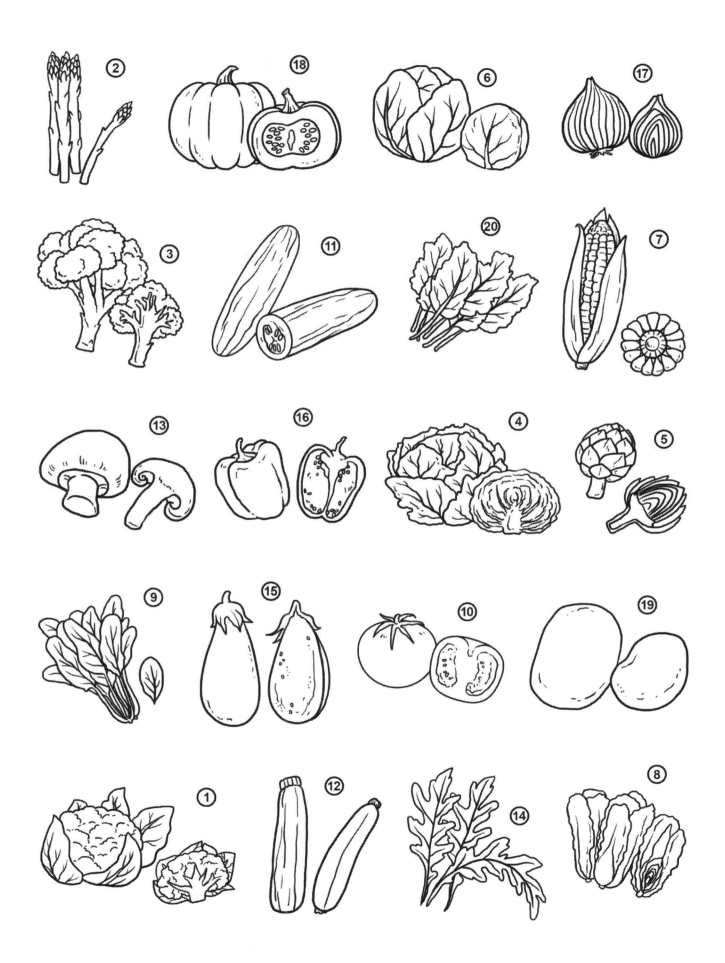

TEKNOLOHIYA (TECHNOLOGY)

1) **móbayl** (mobile)
   MO-bayl

2) **aparáto** (device)
   a-pa-RA-to

3) **kompyúter** (computer)
   kom-PYU-ter

4) **webcám** (webcam)
   web-CAM

5) **flash drive** (flash drive)
   FLASH-drayb

6) **hárd drayv** (hard drive)
   HARD-drayv

7) **mémori kard** (memory card)
   ME-mo-ri-KARD

8) **taga-bása ng kard** (card reader)
   ta-ga-BA-sa-nang-kard

9) **walàng-káwad** (wireless)
   wa-LANG-KA-wad

10) **sólar pánel** (solar panel)
    SO-lar-PA-nel

11) **prínter** (printer)
    PRIN-ter

12) **iskáner** (scanner)
    is-KA-ner

Nakikipagpulong ako sa pamamagitan ng webcam.
I have a meeting via webcam.

Puno ang memory card ng aking kamera.
My camera's memory card is full.

Ise-seyv ko ang mga dokumentong ito sa aking flash drive.
I am going to save these documents on my flash drive.

AGHAM (SCIENCE)

1) **laboratóryo** (laboratory)
   la-bo-ra-TOR-yo

2) **mananaliksík** (researcher)
   ma-na-na-lik-SIK

3) **kalkulasyón** (calculation)
   kal-ku-las-YON

4) **siyentípikó** (scientist)
   si-yen-TI-pi-KO

5) **damít panlaboratóryo** (lab coat)
   da-MIT-pan-la-bo-ra-TOR-yo

6) **éksperiménto** (experiment)
   EKS-pe-ri-MEN-to

7) **pérsonál na kagamitáng pámproteksiyón**
   (personal protective equipment)
   PER-son-NAL-na-ka-ga-mi-TANG-PAM-pro-tek-si-YON

8) **pagsusurì** (test)
   pag-su-su-RI

9) **gantimpalà** (prize)
   gan-tim-pa-LA

10) **pangánib** (risk)
    pa-NGA-nib

11) **instruménto** (instrument)
    ins-tru-MEN-to

12) **estatístiká** (statistics)
    es-ta-TIS-ti-KA

Ang personal na kagamitang pamproteksyon ay sapilitan sa laboratoryo.
Personal protective equipment is mandatory in the laboratory.

Dumating ako para sa isang pagsusuri para sa COVID.
I have come for a COVID test.

Nagtatrabaho siya bilang isang siyentipiko.
He works as a scientist.

ASTRONOMIYA (ASTRONOMY)

1) **téleskópyo** (telescope)
    TE-les-KOP-yo

2) **áraw** (sun)
    A-raw

3) **buwán** (moon)
    bu-WAN

4) **kalawákan** (galaxy)
    ka-la-WA-kan

5) **ásteróyd belt** (asteroid belt)
    AS-te-ROYD-BELT

6) **blak howl** (black hole)
    BLAK-HOWL

7) **eklípse** (eclipse)
    ek-LIP-se

8) **bulalákaw** (shooting star)
    bu-la-LA-kaw

9) **istasyóng pangkalawákan** (space station)
    is-tas-YONG-pang-ka-la-WA-kan

10) **putîng duwénde** (white dwarf)
    pu-TING-du-WEN-de

11) **dambuhalàng pulá** (red giant)
    dam-bu-ha-LANG-pu-LA

12) **órbitá** (orbit)
    OR-bi-TA

13) **konstelasyón** (constellation)
    kons-te-las-YON

14) **enerhíyang madilím** (dark energy)
    e-ner-HI-yang-ma-di-LIM

15) **Plúto** (Pluto)
    PLU-to

16) **Nébulá** (nebula)
    NE-bu-LA

17) **Merkúryo** (Mercury)
    mer-KUR-yo

18) **Bénus** (Venus)
    BE-nus

19) **daigdíg** (Earth)
    da-ig-DIG

20) **Márte** (Mars)
    MAR-te

21) **Húpitér** (Jupiter)
    HU-pi-ter

22) **Satúrno** (Saturn)
    sa-TUR-no

23) **Uráno** (Uranus)
    u-RA-no

24) **Neptúno** (Neptune)
    nep-TU-no

Sa gabi, makikita mo ang buong kalawakan.
At night, you can see the whole galaxy.

Ang istasyong pangkalawakan ay nakarating sa Marte.
The space station landed on Mars.

Nagkaroon ako ng pagkasunog ng balat.
I got a sunburn.

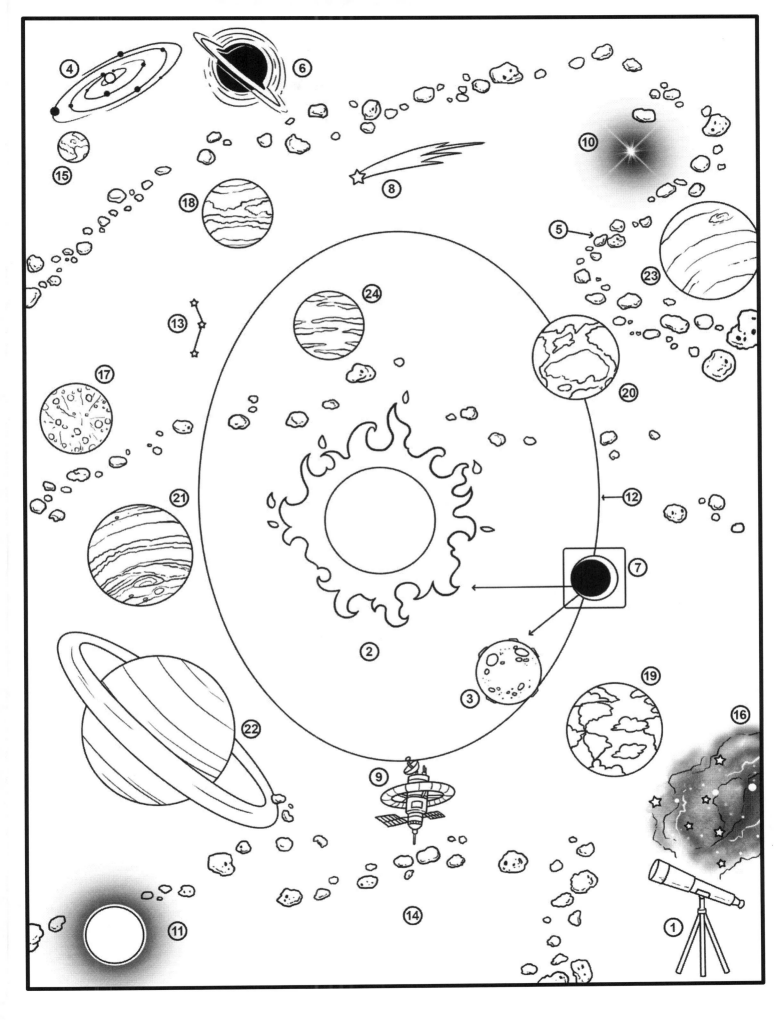

HEOGRAPIYA (GEOGRAPHY)

1) **hilagà** (north)
   hi-la-GA

2) **silángan** (east)
   si-LA-ngan

3) **tímog** (south)
   TI-mog

4) **kanlúran** (west)
   kan-LU-ran

5) **Ékwadór** (Equator)
   EK-wa-DOR

6) **Trópikó ng Kánser** (Tropic of Cancer)
   TRO-pi-ko-nang-KAN-ser

7) **Tropiko ng Kaprikórniyó** (Tropic of Capricorn)
   TRO-pi-ko-nang-kap-ri-KOR-ni-YO

8) **Pólong Tímog** (South Pole)
   PO-long-TI-mog

9) **Pólong Hilagà** (North Pole)
   PO-long- hi-la-GA

10) **Sírkuló Artikó** (Arctic Circle)
    SIR-ku-LO-ar-ti-KO

11) **kontinénte** (continent)
    kon-ti-NEN-te

12) **sa ibáng bansâ** (overseas)
    sa-i-BANG-ban-SA

13) **Apriká** (Africa)
    ap-ri-KA

14) **Ásya** (Asia)
    AS-ya

15) **Hilagáng Amériká** (North America)
    hi-la-GANG-a-ME-ri-KA

16) **Gítnang Amérika** (Central America)
    GIT-nang-a-ME-ri-KA

17) **Tímog Amérika** (South America)
    TI-mog-a-ME-ri-KA

18) **Európa** (Europe)
    yu-RO-pa

19) **Owsyanya** (Oceania)
    ow-SYAN-ya

20) **Antártikó** (Antarctica)
    an-TAR-ti-KO

21) **merídyen** (meridian)
    me-RID-yen

22) **kahílera** (parallel)
    ka-HI-le-ra

23) **Karagatáng Atlántikó** (Atlantic Ocean)
    ka-ra-ga-TANG-at-LAN-ti-ko

24) **Karagatáng Pasípiko** (Pacific Ocean)
    ka-ra-ga-TANG-pa-SI-pi-ko

Nakatira ako sa timog ng Pilipinas.
I live in the south of the Philippines.

Mahilig akong mag-surf sa Karagatang Atlantiko.
I love to surf in the Atlantic Ocean.

Nagplano kami ng paglalakbay sa Europa.
We have planned a trip to Europe.

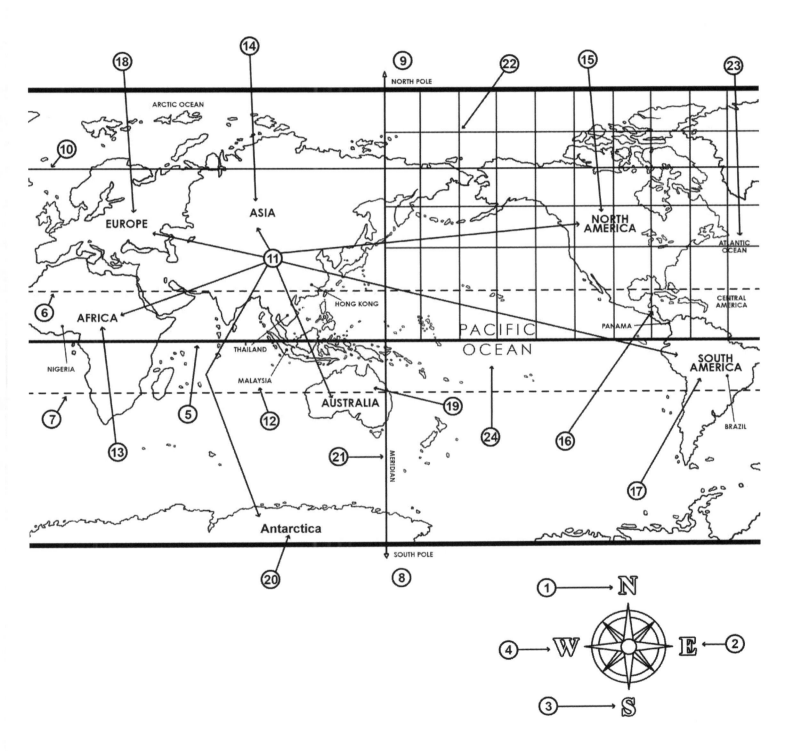

ANG OSPITAL (THE HOSPITAL)

1) **doktór/ manggagámot** (doctor/medic)
dok-TOR/ mang-ga-GA-mot

2) **nars** (nurse)
NARS

3) **ambulánsiyá** (ambulance)
am-bu-LAN-si-YA

4) **pangúnang-lúnas na kit** (first aid kit)
pa-NGU-nang-LU-nas-na-kit

5) **térmométro** (thermometer)
TER-mo-MET-ro

6) **istrétser** (stretcher)
is-TRET-ser

7) **hiringgílya** (syringe)
hi-ring-GIL-ya

8) **karáyom** (needle)
ka-RA-yom

9) **istétoskóp** (stethoscope)
is-TE-tos-KOP

10) **sakláy** (crutch)
sak-LAY

11) **sílyang de-gulóng** (wheelchair)
SIL-yang-de-gu-LONG

12) **silíd ng pagsusúri** (observation room)
si-LID-nang-pag-su-SU-ri

13) **kámang páng-ospitál** (hospital bed)
KA-mang-PANG-os-pi-TAL

14) **ineksiyón** (injection)
i-nek-si-YON

15) **operasyón** (surgery)
o-pe-ras-YON

16) **médikál na kasaysáyan** (medical history)
ME-di-KAL-na-ka-say-SA-yan

17) **pasyénte** (patient)
pas-YEN-te

18) **tablétas** (pill/tablet)
tab-LE-tas

Mayroon akong pakikipagtagpo sa doktor sa Miyerkules.
I have an appointment with the doctor on Wednesday.

Itong kamang pang-ospital ay hindi komportable.
This hospital bed is uncomfortable.

Gustong maging nars ng anak kong babae.
My daughter wants to become a nurse.

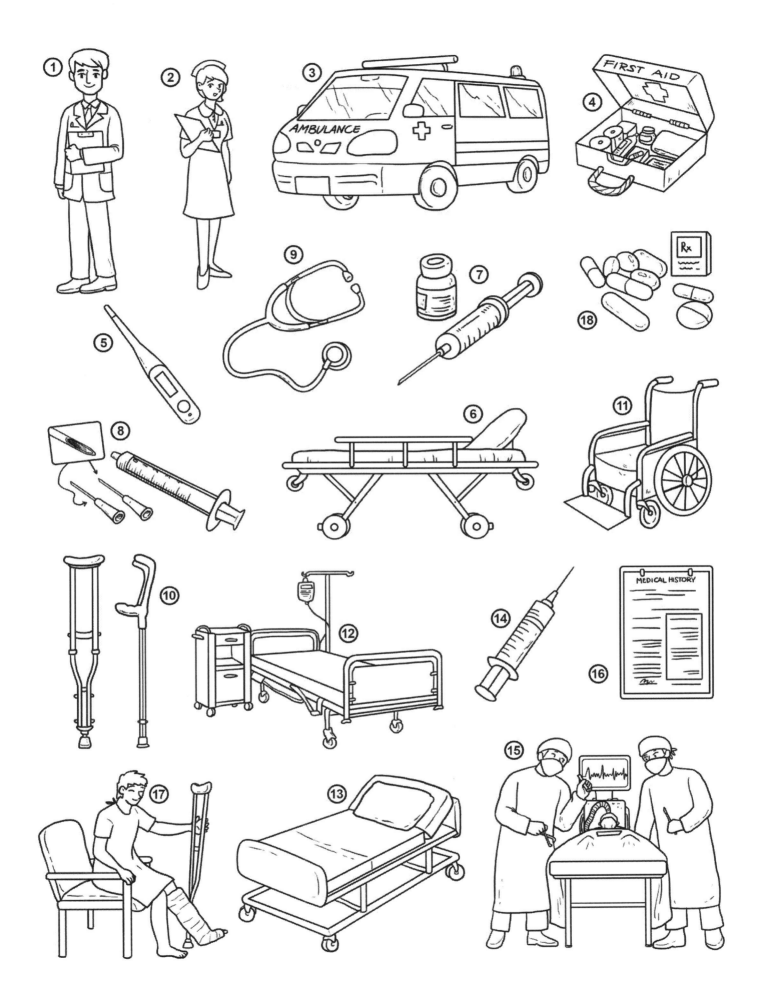

ANG BUKID (THE FARM)

1) **kamálig** (barn)
   ka-MA-lig

2) **kuwádra** (cowshed/stable)
   ku-WAD-ra

3) **magsasaká** (farmer)
   mag-sa-sa-KA

4) **aráro** (plough)
   a-RA-ro

5) **imbákan** (silo)
   im-BA-kan

6) **kiskísan** (mill)
   kis-KI-san

7) **labangán** (water trough)
   la-ba-NGAN

8) **manúkan** (henhouse)
   ma-NU-kan

9) **báhay-pukyútan** (beehive)
   BA-hay-puk-YU-tan

10) **paldó ng dayámi** (hay bale)
    pal-DO-nang-da-YA-mi

11) **báka** (cattle)
    BA-ka

12) **gatásan** (to milk)
    ga-TA-san

13) **káwan** (herd/flock)
    KA-wan

14) **inahíng manók** (hen)
    i-na-HING-ma-NOK

15) **balón** (well)
    ba-LON

16) **sistéma ng patúbig** (irrigation system)
    sis-TE-ma-nang-pa-TU-big

17) **aláy-áy** (scarecrow)
    a-LAY-AY

18) **bakú-bakóng daán** (dirt road)
    ba-KU-ba-KONG-da-AN

Ang aking mga inahing manok ay nangingitlog ng isang dosena sa bawat araw.
My hens lay a dozen eggs per day.

Naglagay ako ng isang alay-ay sa aking bukid para matakot ang mga ibon.
I installed a scarecrow in my field to scare birds away.

Lumiko ka sa kaliwa at sundan ang baku-bakong daan.
Turn left and follow the dirt road.

QUIZ #5

Use arrows to match the corresponding translations:

a. laboratory   1. USB flash drive

b. pear   2. silyang de gulong

c. drums   3. peras

d. north   4. koliplor

e. well   5. presas

f. bagpipes   6. daigdig

g. wheelchair   7. laboratoryo

h. henhouse   8. nars

i. eggplant   9. seresa

j. nurse   10. estatistika

k. Earth   11. bagpayp

l. cauliflower   12. mabuti

m. strawberry   13. hilaga

n. flash drive   14. talong

o. statistics   15. tambol

p. cherry   16. manukan

Fill in the blank spaces with the options below (use each word only once):

Ang mga lolo't lola ko ay nakatira sa _____, _____ ng Copenhagen. Nagpasiya akong bisitahin sila sa susunod na buwan. Hindi namin madalas makita ang isa't isa dahil nakatira ako sa New York, ngunit salamat sa aking _____ at ang aking _____. Ang lola ko ay isang mahusay na tagapagtugtog ng _____. Dati-rati ay naglalaro siya nang live sa mga bar sa paligid ng lungsod. Siya ang nagturo sa akin na tumugtog ng _____!! Ang lolo ko ay _____. Nagpapalago siya ng _____ at mga prutas. Ginagawa Niya ang pinakamainam na _____ at _____ na pie sa mundo.

kompyuter   piyano

usbong ng Bruselas   mansanas

Europa   magsasaka

gitarang de koryente   webcam

rasberi   kanluran

PAGKAIN (FOOD)

1) **pásas** (raisin)
   PA-sas

2) **nogáles** (walnut)
   no-GA-les

3) **karné** (meat)
   kar-NE

4) **túpa** (lamb)
   TU-pa

5) **isdâ** (fish)
   is-DA

6) **manók** (chicken)
   ma-NOK

7) **pábo** (turkey)
   PA-bo

8) **pulút-pukyútan** (honey)
   pu-LUT-puk-YU-tan

9) **asúkal** (sugar)
   a-SU-kal

10) **asín** (salt)
    a-SIN

11) **pamintá** (pepper)
    pa-min-TA

12) **béykon** (bacon)
    BEY-kon

13) **tsoríso** (sausage)
    tso-RI-so

14) **kétsap** (ketchup)
    KET-sap

15) **mayonésa** (mayonnaise)
    ma-yo-NE-sa

16) **mustása** (mustard)
    mus-TA-sa

17) **minátamís** (jam)
    mi-NA-ta-MIS

18) **mantekílya** (butter)
    man-te-KIL-ya

19) **dyus** (juice)
    jus

20) **gátas** (milk)
    GA-tas

Hindi ako makakakain ng fries na walang mayonesa.
I cannot eat fries without mayonnaise.

Ang mga bubuyog ay gumagawa ng pulot-pukyutan.
Bees make honey.

Mas gusto mo ba ang manok o isda?
Do you prefer chicken or fish?

MGA PUTAHE (DISHES)

1) **lasánya** (lasagna)
la-SAN-ya

2) **tórtang patátas** (potato omelette)
TOR-tang-pa-TA-tas

3) **embutído** (meatloaf)
em-bu-TI-do

4) **pinirítong núdels** (fried noodles)
pi-ni-RI-tong-NU-dels

5) **mákaróni at késo** (macaroni and cheese)
MA-ka-RO-ni-at-KE-so

6) **paélya** (paella)
pa-EL-ya

7) **bárbikyú na tadyáng** (barbecue ribs)
BAR-bi-KYU-na-tad-YANG

8) **tinápay na maís** (cornbread)
ti-NA-pay-na-ma-IS

9) **lumpiyâ** (spring roll)
lum-pi-YA

10) **tsísbúrger** (cheeseburger)
TSIS-BUR-ger

11) **prítong manók** (fried chicken)
PRI-tong-ma-NOK

12) **Caesar salad** (Caesar salad)
SE-sar-SA-lad

13) **sibúyas na sópas** (onion soup)
si-BU-yas-na-SO-pas

14) **kólslo** (coleslaw)
KOLS-lo

15) **maangháng na pakpák ng manók** (spicy chicken wings)
ma-ang-HANG-na-pak-PAK-nang-ma-NOK

16) **kúkis na tsokoláte** (chocolate chip cookies)
KU-kis-na-tso-ko-LA-te

17) **ki laym na pastél** (key lime pie)
KI-LAYM-na-pas-TEL

18) **keyk na késo** (cheesecake)
KEYK-na-KE-so

Mahilig ang mga Amerikano sa makaroni at keso.
Americans love macaroni and cheese.

Mag-o-order ako ng sibuyas na sopas.
I am going to order the onion soup.

Keyk na keso ang paborito kong panghimagas.
Cheesecake is my favorite dessert.

PAGKAING-DAGAT (SEAFOOD)

1) **dílis** (anchovy)
   DI-lis

2) **bakaláw** (cod)
   ba-ka-LAW

3) **alimásag** (spider crab)
   a-li-MA-sag

4) **alumáhan** (mackerel)
   a-lu-MA-han

5) **uláng** (lobster)
   u-LANG

6) **kabíbe** (scallop)
   ka-BI-be

7) **máya-máya** (snapper)
   MA-ya-MA-ya

8) **itlóg ng salmón** (salmon roe)
   it-LOG-nang-sal-MON

9) **alimángo** (crab)
   a-li-MA-ngo

10) **molúsko** (shellfish)
    mo-LUS-ko

11) **ígat** (eel)
    I-gat

12) **hípon** (shrimp)
    HI-pon

Gusto ko ang mga dilis sa aking pizza.
I want anchovies on my pizza.

Ang mga kabibi ay napakamahal.
Scallops are very expensive.

Bumili ako ng salmong Eskoses para sa hapunan.
I bought Scottish salmon for dinner.

MGA HUGIS (SHAPES)

1) **bilóg** (circle)
   bi-LOG

2) **habilóg** (oval)
   ha-bi-LOG

3) **tatsulók** (triangle)
   tat-su-LOK

4) **parihabâ** (rectangle)
   pa-ri-ha-BA

5) **parisukát** (square)
   pa-ri-su-KAT

6) **trapeséyo** (trapezoid)
   tra-pe-SE-yo

7) **rómbus** (rhombus)
   ROM-bus

8) **kúbo** (cube)
   KU-bo

9) **pentagonó** (pentagon)
   pen-ta-go-NO

10) **ekságonó** (hexagon)
    ek-SA-go-NO

11) **palasó** (arrow)
    pa-la-SO

12) **krus** (cross)
    KRUS

13) **púso** (heart)
    PU-so

14) **bituín** (star)
    bi-tu-IN

15) **silíndro** (cylinder)
    si-LIN-dro

16) **kóno** (cone)
    KO-no

17) **pirámide** (pyramid)
    pi-RA-mide

18) **espéra** (sphere)
    es-PE-ra

19) **prísma** (prism)
    PRIS-ma

Nabisita mo ba ang piramide ng Louvre?
Have you visited the Louvre pyramid?

Ang anak ko ay mahilig maglaro ng mga kubo.
My baby loves to play with cubes.

Ang kalsada ay nakasara, mayroong mga kono sa sahig.
The road is shut, there are cones on the ground.

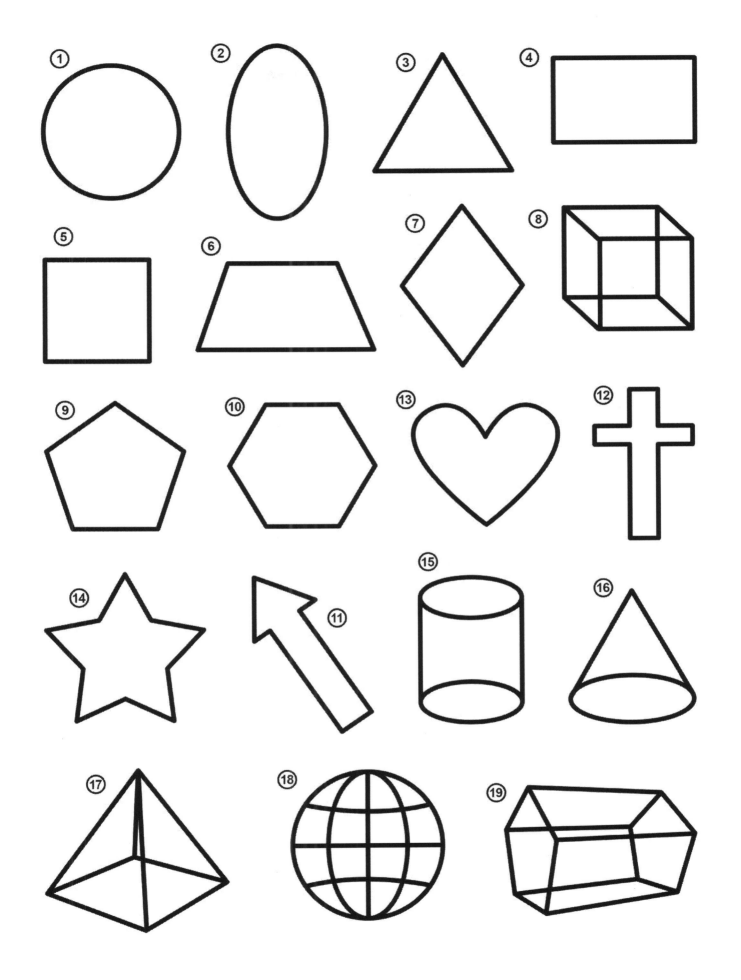

ANG PAMILIHAN (THE SUPERMARKET)

1) **karitón** (shopping cart)
   ka-ri-TON-sa-pa-mi-mi-LI

2) **éskaparáte** (cabinet/display case)
   ES-ka-pa-RA-te

3) **mamimíli** (customer)
   ma-mi-MI-li

4) **kahéro/kahéra** (cashier, male/female)
   ka-HE-ro/ka-HE-ra

5) **resíbo** (receipt)
   re-SI-bo

6) **panaderyá** (bakery)
   pa-na-der-YA

7) **mga prútas at gúlay** (fruits and vegetables)
   ma-nga-PRU-tas-at-GU-lay

8) **karné** (meat)
   kar-NE

9) **prodúkto ng gátas** (dairy products)
   pro-DUK-to-nang-GA-tas

10) **isdâ** (fish)
    is-DA

11) **eládong pagkáin** (frozen food)
    e-LA-dong-pag-KA-in

12) **manúkan** (poultry)
    ma-NU-kan

13) **legúmbre** (legumes)
    le-GUM-bre

14) **meryénda** (snacks)
    mer-YEN-da

15) **panghimágas** (dessert)
    pang-hi-MA-gas

16) **inúmin** (drinks)
    i-NU-min

17) **gámit sa báhay** (household items)
    GA-mit-sa-BA-hay

18) **mákináng panghákot** (belt conveyor)
    MA-ki-NANG-pang-HA-kot

Kinukuha ko ang aking tinapay sa panaderya tuwing umaga.
I go to get my bread at the bakery every morning.

Hindi ako kumakain ng karne.
I do not eat meat.

Ang tindahang ito ay may samu't-saring uri ng mga prutas at gulay.
This shop has a great selection of fruits and vegetables.

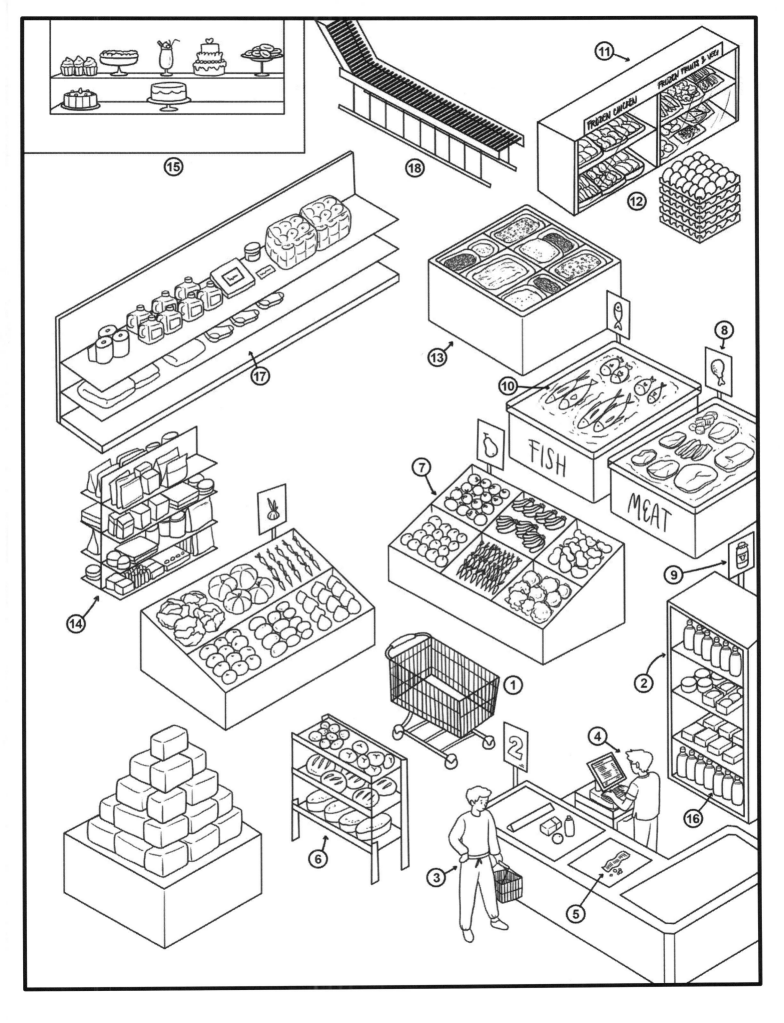

MEDIA (MEDIA)

1) **mágasín** (magazine)
   MA-ga-SIN

2) **fax** (fax)
   FAX

3) **talàarawán** (journal)
   ta-LA-a-ra-WAN

4) **koreó** (postal mail)
   ko-re-YO

5) **líham** (letter)
   LI-ham

6) **rádyo** (radio)
   RAD-yo

7) **kómiks** (comic)
   KO-miks

8) **aklát** (book)
   ak-LAT

9) **potógrapíya** (photography)
   po-TO-gra-PI-ya

10) **landláyn** (landline phone)
    land-LAYN

11) **télebisyón** (TV)
    TE-le-bis-YON

12) **pelíkulá** (movie)
    pe-LI-ku-LA

13) **móbayl na teléponó/sélpon** (mobile phone/cell phone)
    MO-bayl-na- te-LE-po-NO /SEL-pon

14) **wikàng pasényas** (sign language)
    wi-KANG-pa-SEN-yas

Ang konsiyerto ni Beyonce ay ipalalabas sa telebisyon bukas ng gabi.
Beyoncé's concert airs on TV tomorrow night.

Pwede mo bang ibigay sa akin ang numero ng iyong selpon?
Can you give me your cell number?

Pinadalhan ko siya ng sulat.
I have sent him a letter.

ANG PERYA / ANG PARKENG LIBANGAN (THE FAIR/THE AMUSEMENT PARK)

1) **baháy ng mga salamín** (house of mirrors)
ba-HAY-nang-ma-NGA-sa-la-MIN

2) **sasakyáng-dágat ng piráta (**pirate ship/boat swing)
sa-sak-YANG-DA-gat-nang-pi-RA-ta

3) **bílihan ng tíket** (ticket booth)
BI-li-han-nang-TI-ket

4) **pagsakáy sa ugóy** (swing ride)
pag-sa-KAY-sa-u-GOY

5) **róler kówster** (roller coaster)
RO-ler-KOWS-ter

6) **tsubíbo** (Ferris wheel)
tsu-BI-bo

7) **tsubíbo** (carousel/merry-go-round)
tsu-BI-bo

8) **bámper na kótse** (bumper cars)
BAM-per-na-KOT-se

9) **tasá ng tsaá at platíto** (teacups/cup and saucer)
ta-SA-nang-tsa-A-at-pla-TI-to

10) **pénduló** (pendulum)
PEN-du-LO

11) **arkádang silíd** (arcade room)
ar-KA-dang-si-LID

12) **korn dog** (corn dog)
KORN-DOG

13) **kóno ng isnów** (snow cone)
KO-no-nang-is-NOW

14) **kóton kéndi** (cotton candy)
KO-ton-KEN-di

15) **kénding mansánas** (candy apple)
KEN-ding-man-SA-nas

Gusto ko ang roler kowster.
I love roller coasters.

Nawala siya sa bahay ng mga salamin.
He got lost in the house of mirrors.

Kumain ako ng sobrang daming koton kendi.
I ate too much cotton candy.

MGA PANGYAYARI SA BUHAY (LIFE EVENTS)

1) **kapanganákan** (birth)
   ka-pa-nga-NA-kan

2) **binyágan** (christening/baptism)
   bin-YA-gan

3) **únang áraw ng páaralán** (first day of school)
   U-nang-A-raw-nang-PA-a-ra-LAN

4) **makipagkaibígan** (make friends)
   ma-ki-pag-ka-i-BI-gan

5) **kaarawán** (birthday)
   ka-a-ra-WAN

6) **umiíbig** (fall in love)
   u-mi-I-big

7) **pagtatapós** (graduation)
   pag-ta-ta-POS

8) *magsimulâ sa unibérsidád* (to start university/begin college)
   mag-si-mu-LA-sa-u-ni-ber-si-DAD

9) **makapagtrabáho** (get a job)
   ma-ka-pag-tra-BA-ho

10) **magíng negósyánte** (become an entrepreneur)
    ma-GING-ne-GOS-YAN-te

11) **maglakbáy sa buông mundó** (travel around the world)
    mag-lak-BAY-sa-bu-ONG-mun-DO

12) **magpakásal** (get married)
    mag-pa-KA-sal

13) **magkaanák** (have a baby)
    mag-ka-a-NAK

14) **ipagdíwang ang kaarawán** (celebrate a birthday)
    i-pag-DI-wang-ang-ka-a-ra-WAN

15) **pagreretíro** (retirement)
    pag-re-re-TI-ro

16) **kamatáyan** (death)
    ka-ma-TA-yan

Magpapakasal na ako sa susunod na buwan.
I am going to get married next month.

Ang mga magulang ko ay retirado na.
My parents are retired.

Nakahanap na sa wakas si Gabrielle ng trabaho.
Gabrielle has finally found a job.

MGA PANG-URI I (ADJECTIVES I)

1) **malakí** (big)
ma-la-KI

2) **maliít** (small)
ma-li-IT

3) **malakás** (loud)
ma-la-KAS

4) **tahímik** (silent)
ta-HI-mik

5) **mahabâ** (long)
ma-ha-BA

6) **maiklî** (short)
ma-ik-LI

7) **maláwak** (wide)
ma-LA-wak

8) **makítid** (narrow)
ma-KI-tid

9) **mahál** (expensive)
ma-HAL

10) **múra** (cheap)
MU-ra

11) **mabilís** (fast)
ma-bi-LIS

12) **mabágal** (slow)
ma-BA-gal

13) **waláng-lamán** (empty)
wa-LANG-la-MAN

14) **punô** (full)
pu-NO

15) **malambót** (soft)
ma-lam-BOT

16) **matigás** (hard)
ma-ti-GAS

17) **mataás** (tall)
ma-ta-AS

18) **maiklî** (short)
ma-ik-LI

Ang aso ng kapitbahay ay napaka-ingay.
The neighbor's dog is very noisy.

Ang restawran na ito ay maganda at mura.
This restaurant is good and cheap.

Ang tsite ay ang pinakamabilis na hayop.
The cheetah is the fastest animal.

QUIZ #6

Use arrows to match the corresponding translations:

a. book

b. dairy products

c. roller coaster

d. eel

e. circle

f. anchovy

g. jam

h. cotton candy

i. carousel

j. turkey

k. drinks

l. cross

m. nuts

n. fish

o. onion soup

p. arrow

1. inumin

2. igat

3. mani

4. isda

5. sibuyas na sopas

6. pabo

7. produkto ng gatas

8. krus

9. roler kowster

10. palaso

11. aklat

12. minatamis

13. koton kendi

14. dilis

15. bilog

16. tsubibo

Fill in the blank spaces with the options below (use each word only once):

Nag-organisa ng masarap na handaan si Pauline at ang kanyang mga kaibigan matapos ang kanilang seremonya ng _____ noong nakaraang katapusan ng linggo. Sa Setyembre, lahat sila ay pupunta para _____ maliban kay Pauline dahil gusto niyang _____. Siya ay papasok sa susunod pang taon. Ang menu ay napaka-_____, ngunit ang pagkain ay nagkakahalaga ng ganito. Masarap iyon. Bilang pauna, mayroong _____ at _____. Masaya si Pauline dahil gustong-gusto niya ang pagkaing-dagat. Pagkatapos ay naroon ang pangunahing kurso. Nakapili sila sa pagitan ng _____ at ng_____ sa_____. Pinili ni Pauline ang manok ngunit sa kasamaang-palad ito ay medyo _____at nagkulang ng_____. Para sa _____, nagpakabusog sila sa isang masarap na tsokolateng fondant.

mustasa

mahal

pagtatapos

matigas

asin

kabibe

panghimagas

lasagna

alimango

manok

magsimula sa unibersidad

maglakbay sa buong mundo

138

MGA PANG-URI II (ADJECTIVES II)

1) **bágo** (new)
BA-go

2) **lumâ** (old)
lu-MA

3) **maginháwa** (comfortable)
ma-gin-HA-wa

4) **hindî maginháwa** (uncomfortable)
hin-DI-ma-gin-HA-wa

5) **mapangánib** (dangerous)
ma-pa-NGA-nib

6) **nakakayamót** (annoying)
na-ka-ka-ya-MOT

7) **maalóg** (shaky)
ma-a-LOG

8) **kumpléto** (complete)
kum-PLE-to

9) **kúlang** (incomplete)
KU-lang

10) **sirâ** (broken)
si-RA

11) **marilág** (gorgeous)
ma-ri-LAG

12) **marangál** (virtuous)
ma-ra-NGAL

13) **magkatúlad** (similar)
mag-ka-TU-lad

14) **magkáibá** (different)
mag-KA-i-BA

15) **bukás** (open)
bu-KAS

16) **sarádo** (closed)
sa-RA-do

Ang kambal na iyon ay magkatulad na magkatulad.
Those twins are very similar.

Ang aking sopa ay luma subalit maginhawa.
My sofa is old but comfortable.

Ang tindahang ito ay hindi na naging bukas!
This shop is never open!

MGA PANG-ABAY (ADVERBS)

1) **díto** (here)
DI-to

2) **doón** (there)
do-ON

3) **malápit** (near)
ma-LA-pit

4) **malayô** (far)
ma-la-YO

5) **taás** (up)
ta-AS

6) **babâ** (down)
ba-BA

7) **loób** (inside)
lo-OB

8) **labás** (outside)
la-BAS

9) **naúna** (ahead)
na-u-U-na

10) **sa likód** (behind)
sa-li-KOD

11) **hindî** (no)
hin-DI

12) **óo** (yes)
O-o

13) **ngayón** (now)
nga-YON

14) **mabúti** (well/good/right)
ma-BU-ti

15) **masamâ** (bad/wrong)
ma-sa-MA

Hinihintay kita sa ibaba.
I am waiting for you downstairs.

Tawagan mo ako ngayon.
Call me now.

Kumakain ba tayo dito o doon?
Are we eating here or over there?

MGA DIREKSIYON (DIRECTIONS)

1) **blóke** (block)
   BLO-ke

2) **liwásan** (square)
   li-WA-san

3) **párke** (park)
   PAR-ke

4) **sábwey** (subway)
   SAB-wey

5) **kánto** (corner)
   KAN-to

6) **abenída** (avenue)
   a-be-NI-da

7) **kálye** (street)
   KAL-ye

8) **sakáyan ng bus** (bus stop)
   sa-KA-yan-nang-BUS

9) **ílaw trápikó** (traffic lights)
   I-law-TRA-pi-KO

10) **tawíran** (crossing/crosswalk)
    ta-WI-ran

11) **taás** (up)
    ta-AS

12) **babâ** (down)
    ba-BA

13) **kaliwâ** (left)
    ka-li-WA

14) **kánan** (right)
    KA-nan

15) **palátandaan sa dáan** (road signs)
    pa-LA-tan-da-an-sa-DA-an

16) **pulís trápikó** (traffic police)
    pu-LIS-TRA-pi-KO

Hindi ko gusto ang amoy ng subwey.
I do not like the smell of the subway.

Dumaan ka sa ikalawang kalye sa kaliwa.
Take the second street on the left.

Dapat mong gamitin ang tawiran.
You must use the crosswalk.

ANG RESTAWRAN (THE RESTAURANT)

1) **tagapamahálâ** (manager)
   ta-ga-pa-ma-HA-la

2) **mésa** (table)
   ME-sa

3) **putáhe** (menu)
   pu-TA-he

4) **pinggán** (dish)
   ping-GAN

5) **pampagána** (appetizer)
   pam-pa-GA-na

6) **istárter** (starter)
   is-TAR-ter

7) **pángunáhing putáhe** (main course)
   PA-ngu-NA-hing-pu-TA-he

8) **pánghimagás** (dessert)
   PANG-hi-ma-GAS

9) **kumakáin** (diner)
   ku-ma-KA-in

10) **kúsinéro** (cook)
    KU-si-NE-ro

11) **wéyter** (waiter)
    WEY-ter

12) **wéytres** (waitress)
    WEYT-res

13) **tip** (tip)
    TIP

14) **mataás na upúan** (high chair)
    ma-ta-AS-na-u-PU-an

15) **listáhan ng álak** (wine list)
    lis-TA-han-nang-A-lak

16) **tagapaglutò ng pástelerya** (pastry chef)
    ta-ga-pag-lu-TO-nang-PAS-te-ler-ya

Gusto mo bang makita ang aming putahe?
Would you like to see our menu?

Pakisuyo sana akong bigyan ng pampagana.
I will have an appetizer, please.

Batiin ang iyong tagapagluto!
Congratulate your chef!

ANG MALL (THE MALL)

1) **palapág** (floor)
   pa-la-PAG

2) **akwáryum** (aquarium)
   ak-WAR-yum

3) **kainán** (food court)
   ka-i-NAN

4) **élebéytor** (elevator)
   E-le-BEY-tor

5) **eskaládor** (escalator)
   es-ka-LA-dor

6) **labásang páng-sakunâ** (emergency exit)
   la-BA-sang-PANG-sa-ku-NA

7) **párlor** (beauty salon)
   PAR-lor

8) **tindáhan ng damít** (clothing store)
   tin-DA-han-nang-da-MIT

9) **pálarùan** (playground)
   PA-la-RU-an

10) **guwárdiyá** (security guard)
    gu-WAR-di-YA

11) **kámerá sa pagmanmán** (surveillance camera)
    KA-me-RA-sa-pag-man-MAN

12) **panaderyá** (bakery)
    pa-na-der-YA

13) **tindáhan ng pálakásan** (sports store)
    tin-DA-han-nang-PA-la-KA-san

14) **fáwnteyn** (fountain)
    FAWN-teyn

Sumakay sa elebeytor at huminto sa ikalawang palapag.
Take the elevator and stop on the second floor.

Dadalhin ko ang anak kong lalaki sa palaruan.
I am going to take my son to the playground.

Nakatira ako katabi ng tindahan ng palakasan.
I live next to the sports store.

MGA PANDIWA I (VERBS I)

1) **makipag-úsap** (to talk)
ma-ki-pag-U-sap

2) **uminóm** (to drink)
u-mi-NOM

3) **kumáin** (to eat)
ku-MA-in

4) **maglakád** (to walk)
mag-la-KAD

5) **magbukás** (to open)
mag-bu-KAS

6) **magsará** (to close)
mag-sa-RA

7) **magbigáy** (to give)
mag-bi-GAY

8) **makíta** (to see)
ma-KI-ta

9) **sumunód** (to follow)
su-mu-NOD

10) **yumákap** (to hug)
yu-MA-kap

11) **humalík** (to kiss)
hu-ma-LIK

12) **bumilí** (to buy)
bu-mi-LI

13) **makiníg** (to listen)
ma-ki-NIG

14) **kumantá** (to sing)
ku-man-TA

15) **sumayáw** (to dance)
su-ma-YAW

Dapat mong isara ang bintana.
You must close the window.

Sumunod kayo sa akin!
Follow me!

Magbigay ka sa kanya ng 10 euro.
Give him 10 euros.

MGA PANDIWA II (VERBS II)

1) **magsulát** (to write)
   mag-su-LAT

2) **magbasá** (to read)
   mag-ba-SA

3) **maglínis** (to clean)
   mag-LI-nis

4) **mamúlot** (to pick up)
   ma-MU-lot

5) **maghanáp** (to find)
   mag-ha-NAP

6) **maghúgas** (to wash)
   mag-HU-gas

7) **manoód** (to watch)
   ma-no-OD

8) **mag-áyos** (to fix)
   mag-A-yos

9) **mag-isíp** (to think)
   mag-i-SIP

10) **kumúha** (to take)
    ku-MU-ha

11) **magpútol** (to cut)
    mag-PU-tol

12) **humintô** (to stop)
    hu-min-TO

13) **umiyák** (to cry)
    u-mi-YAK

14) **ngumitî** (to smile)
    ngu-mi-TI

15) **tumúlong** (to help)
    tu-MU-long

Huminto ka sa pag-iyak.
Stop crying.

Maglilinis ako ng aking apartment.
I am going to clean my flat.

Inayos ko ang makina ng aking kotse.
I have repaired my car's engine.

KONSTRUKSIYON I (CONSTRUCTION I)

1) **grúwa** (crane)
GRU-wa

2) **házard teyp** (hazard tape)
HA-zard- TEYP

3) **kóno pantrapiko** (traffic cone)
KO-no-pan-tra-PI-ko

4) **pála** (construction shovel)
PA-la

5) **martílyo** (hammer)
mar-TIL-yo

6) **pamútol ng káwad** (wire cutters)
pa-MU-tol-nang-KA-wad

7) **róler ng pintúra** (paint roller)
RO-ler-nang-pin-TU-ra

8) **chainsaw** (chainsaw)
TSEYN-so

9) **baréna** (drill)
ba-RE-na

10) **jakhámmer** (jackhammer)
jak-HAM-mer

11) **pláis** (pliers)
PLA-is

12) **distórnilyadór** (screwdriver)
dis-TOR-nil-ya-DOR

Ang chainsaw ay napakaingay.
The chainsaw is too loud.

Kailangan ko ng martilyo para maisabit ang larawang ito.
I need a hammer to hang this picture.

Ibigay mo sa akin ang distornilyador.
Give me the screwdriver.

KONSTRUKSIYON II (CONSTRUCTION II)

1) **túlbax** (toolbox)
   TUL-bax

2) **sombrérong pámproteksyón** (work helmet/hard hat)
   som-BRE-rong-PAM-pro-tek-SYON

3) **pláno** (blueprint)
   PLA-no

4) **túbo** (pipe)
   TU-bo

5) **dulós** (trowel)
   du-LOS

6) **panghalò ng seménto** (concrete mixer)
   pang-ha-LO-nang-se-MEN-to

7) **ladrílyo** (brick)
   lad-RIL-yo

8) **materyáles pángkonstruksyón** (building materials)
   ma-ter-YA-les-PANG-kons-truk-SYON

9) **baldósa** (tiles)
   bal-DO-sa

10) **seménto** (cement)
    se-MEN-to

11) **buhángin** (sand)
    bu-HA-ngin

12) **grába** (gravel)
    GRA-ba

Ang mga bahay-Ingles ay gawa sa ladrilyo.
English houses are made of bricks.

Ang aking tulbax ay nasa garahe.
My toolbox is in the garage.

Nagbaba kami ng graba sa aming harapang bakuran.
We have put gravel down in our front yard.

QUIZ #7

Use arrows to match the corresponding translations:

a. waitress   1. makipag-usap

b. left   2. bukas

c. old   3. malayo

d. bus stop   4. kumanta

e. bad   5. kanan

f. playground   6. palaruan

g. right   7. elebeytor

h. to talk   8. panaderya

i. main course   9. sarado

j. closed   10. bumili

k. to sing   11. kaliwa

l. elevator   12. masama

m. to buy   13. matanda

n. open   14. weytres

o. bakery   15. sakayan ng bus

p. far   16. pangunahing putahe

Fill in the blank spaces with the options below (use each word only once):

Narito ang mga direksyon para makarating sa _____ mula sa lugar ng_____. Kailangan mong _____ sa unang kalye sa_____at pumunta sa_____. Kapag ang ilaw ay berde, lumiko sa kaliwa. _____ ng simbahan, mayroong isang istasyon ng _____. Bagtasin ang istasyon at ito ay magdadala sa iyo para _____ sa loob ng 10 minuto. Makikita mo ang tindahan sa iyong kaliwa.

ilaw trapiko   tindahan ng damit

maglakad   kanan

fawnten   lumiko

Sa likod   sabwey

MGA HALAMAN AT PUNO (PLANTS AND TREES)

1) **ligáw na bulaklák** (wildflower)
   li-GAW-na-bulak-LAK

2) **halámang-gamót** (herb)
   ha-LA-mang-ga-MOT

3) **kabuté** (mushroom)
   ka-bu-TE

4) **damó** (weed)
   da-MO

5) **lató** (seaweed)
   la-TO

6) **pakó** (fern)
   pa-KO

7) **tambô** (reed)
   tam-BO

8) **kawáyan** (bamboo)
   ka-WA-yan

9) **galamáy-amô** (ivy)
   ga-la-MAY-a-MO

10) **lúmot** (moss)
    LU-mot

11) **damó** (grass)
    da-MO

12) **palméra** (palm tree)
    pal-ME-ra

13) **bakáwan** (mangrove)
    ba-KA-wan

14) **kákto** (cactus)
    KAK-to

Niregaluhan niya ako ng isang bungkos ng mga ligaw na bulaklak.
He gifted me a bouquet of wildflowers.

Ang kawayan ay lumalaki nang napakabilis.
Bamboo grows very fast.

Sa gabing ito, kami ay kumakain ng pastang sinahugan ng kabute.
Tonight, we are eating mushroom pasta.

ANG KARNABAL (THE CARNIVAL)

1) **máskará** (mask)
MAS-ka-RA

13) **kóstyum** (costume/disguise)
KOS-tyum

14) **balsá** (float)
bal-SA

15) **bulaklák** (flowers)
bu-lak-LAK

16) **tamból na isnéyr** (snare drum)
tam-BOL-na-is-NEYR

17) **payáso** (clown)
pa-YA-so

18) **superhíro** (superhero)
su-per-HI-ro

19) **prinsésa** (princess)
prin-SE-sa

20) **ástronót** (astronaut)
AS-tro-NOT

21) **manggagáya** (mime)
mang-ga-GA-ya

22) **bilanggô** (prisoner)
bi-lang-GO

23) **kasangkápan sa báháy** (household appliance)
ka-sang-KA-pan-sa-BA-hay

13) **diwatà** (fairy)
di-wa-TA

14) **mágtotrosó** (lumberjack)
MAG-to-tro-SO

Nagbabasa ako sa aking anak ng kuwento tungkol sa diwata bawat gabi.
I read a fairy tale to my daughter every evening.

Dapat kang magsuot ng isang maskara sa ospital.
You must wear a mask in the hospital.

Si Diana ay ang naging prinsesa ng mga tao.
Diana was the people's princess.

ANG PAGAWAAN (THE WORKSHOP)

1) **kasangkápan** (tool)
oo-TEE

2) **paggawâ ng siyáhan** (saddlery)
pag-ga-WA-nang-si-YA-han

3) **kárpintérya** (carpentry/woodwork)
KAR-pin-TER-ya

4) **tapíseríya** (upholstery/tapestry)
ta-PI-se-RI-ya

5) **paggawâ ng sapátos**
(shoemaking/shoerepair)
pag-ga-WA-nang-sa-PA-tos

6) **pandáy-pílak** (silversmith)
pan-DAY-PI-lak

7) **pandáy** (blacksmith)
pan-DAY

8) **mekánikó** (mechanic)
me-KA-ni-KO

9) **téla** (textile)
TE-la

10) **panaderyá** (bakery)
pa-na-der-YA

11) **aláhas pang-kóstyum** (costume jewelry)
a-LA-has-pang-KOS-tyum

12) **sapín sa paá** (footwear)
sa-PIN-sa-pa-A

13) **pagpápanatili** (maintenance)
pag-PA-pa-na-ti-li

14) **pagkukumpuní** (repair)
pag-ku-kum-pu-NI

15) **laráwan** (painting)
la-RA-wan

16) **pástelerya** (pastry)
PAS-te-ler-ya

Natapos na kumpunihin ng mekaniko ang aking kotse.
The mechanic has finished repairing my car.

Ako ang tauhan sa pagpapanatili.
I am the maintenance guy.

Gusto kong bilhin ang iyong pinintang larawan.
I would like to buy your painting.

ANG TINDAHAN NG GROSERI (THE GROCERY STORE)

1) **pásta** (pasta)
   PAS-ta

2) **bigás** (rice)
   BI-gas

3) **abéna** (oat)
   a-BE-na

4) **tinápay** (bread)
   ti-NA-pay

5) **mantikà** (oils)
   man-ti-KA

6) **sársa** (sauces)
   SAR-sa

7) **pampalása sa ensaláda** (salad dressings)
   pam-pa-LA-sa-sa-en-sa-LA-da

8) **rekádo** (condiments)
   re-KA-do

9) **de-láta** (canned goods)
   de-LA-ta

10) **hamón** (ham)
    ha-MON

11) **késo** (cheese)
    KE-so

12) **peanut butter** (peanut butter)
    PI-nat-BA-ter

13) **kéndi** (candy)
    KEN-di

14) **bins** (beans)
    BINS

15) **kapé** (coffee)
    ka-PE

24) **tsaá** (tea)
    tsa-A

Gusto kong kumain ng sandwits na may peanut butter.
I want to eat a peanut butter sandwich.

Naglalagay ako ng gatas ng abena sa aking kape.
I take oat milk in my coffee.

Matatagpuan mo ang mga pinakamasasarap na keso sa mundo sa Pransiya.
You can find the best cheeses in the world in France.

PAGLALAKBAY AT PAMUMUHAY I (TRAVEL AND LIVING I)

1) **púnong abalá** (host)
   PU-nong-a-ba-LA

2) **turísta** (tourist)
   tu-RIS-ta

3) **manlalakbáy** (traveler)
   man-la-lak-BAY

4) **bagáhe** (luggage)
   ba-GA-he

5) **bitbít na bagáhe** (hand luggage)
   bit-BIT-na-ba-GA-he

6) **kámera** (camera)
   KA-me-ra

7) **otél** (hotel)
   o-TEL

8) **dormitóryo** (hostel)
   dor-mi-TOR-yo

9) **tabérna** (bed & breakfast/inn)
   ta-BER-na

10) **kábin** (cabin)
    KA-bin

11) **tólda** (tent)
    TOL-da

12) **paglipád** (flight)
    pag-li-PAD

13) **pag-alís** (departure)
    pag-a-LIS

14) **pagdatíng** (arrival)
    pag-da-TING

Nag-book ako ng isang taberna para sa tatlong gabi.
I booked a bed and breakfast for three nights.

Ang paglipad ng eroplano ay sa 1:30 ng hapon.
The flight departs at 1:30 p.m.

Huwag mong kalimutan ang kamera!
Do not forget the camera!

PAGLALAKBAY AT PAMUMUHAY II (TRAVEL AND LIVING II)

1) **báyan** (town)
BA-yan

2) **mápa** (map)
MA-pa

3) **sakáyan ng bus** (bus stop)
sa-KA-yan-nang-BUS

4) **táksi** (taxi)
TAK-si

5) **arkiláhan ng kótse** (car rental)
ar-ki-LA-han-nang-KOT-se

6) **istasyón ng tren** (train station)
is-tas-YON-nang-TREN

7) **pálipáran** (airport)
PA-li-PA-ran

8) **pasapórte** (passport)
pa-sa-POR-te

9) **kard ng pagkákakilanlán**
(ID/identification card)
KARD-nang-pag-KA-ka-ki-lan-LAN

10) **salapî** (currency)
sa-la-PI

12) **péra** (cash)
PE-ra

13) **debit card** (debit card)
de-BIT-kard

14) **credit card** (credit card)
kre-DIT-kard

15) **gabáy ng turísta** (tourist guide)
ga-BAY-nang-tu-RISta

Dapat kong mapanibago ang aking pasaporte.
I must renew my passport.

Nagbabayad ka ba sa pamamagitan ng debit card o pera?
Are you paying by debit card or cash?

Maaari ka bang mag-book ng isang taksi para sa akin?
Could you book a taxi for me?

MGA LARUAN (TOYS)

1) **bóla** (ball)
   BO-la

2) **tédi beyr** (teddy bear)
   TE-di-BEYR

3) **tren** (train)
   TREN

4) **iskéytbord** (skateboard)
   is-KEYT-bord

5) **manikà** (doll)
   man-yi-KA

6) **kótseng pangkaréra** (race car)
   KOT-seng-pang-ka-RE-ra

7) **róbot** (robot)
   RO-bot

8) **saranggóla** (kite)
   sa-rang-GO-la

9) **tamból** (drum)
   tam-BOL

10) **húla hup** (hula hoop)
    HU-la-HUP

11) **bagón** (wagon)
    ba-GON

12) **blóke** (blocks)
    BLO-ke

13) **silóponó** (xylophone)
    si-LO-po-NO

14) **trak** (truck)
    TRAK

15) **eropláno** (airplane)
    e-ro-PLA-no

16) **ladrílyo** (bricks)
    lad-RIL-yo

Natutunan kong tumugtog ng mga tambol 10 taon na ang nakaraan.
I learned to play the drums 10 years ago.

Nawala ang tedi beyr ng aking anak na babae.
My daughter has lost her teddy bear.

Ihagis mo sa akin ang bola!
Throw me the ball!

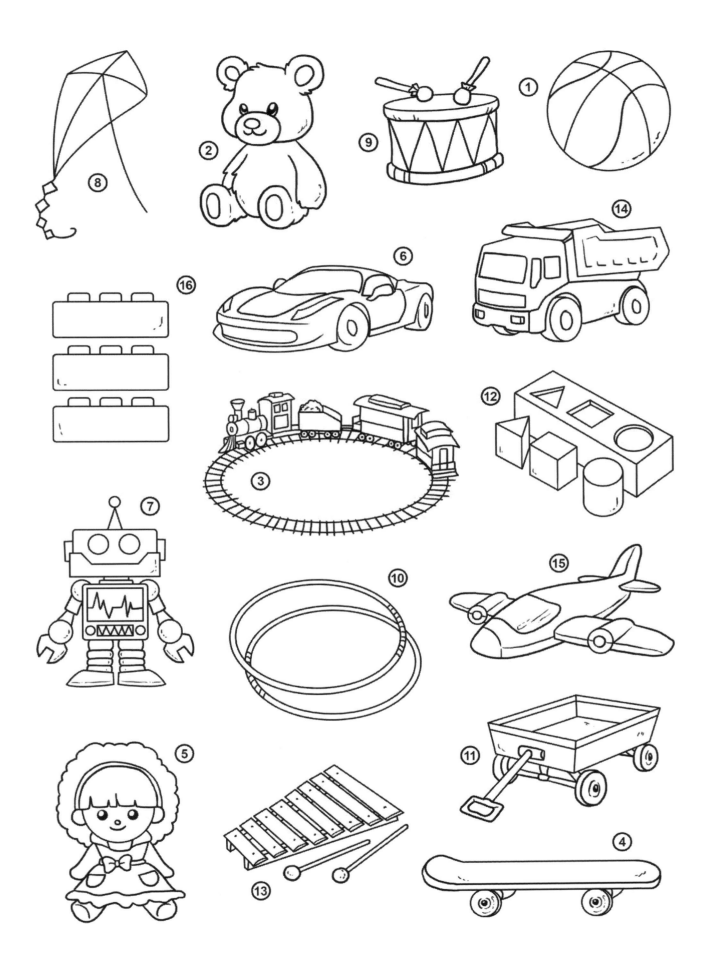

ANG PAGDIRIWANG NG KAARAWAN (THE BIRTHDAY PARTY)

1) **báner ng kaarawán** (birthday banner)
BA-ner-nang-ka-a-ra-WAN

2) **dekorasyón** (decoration)
de-ko-ras-YON

3) **regálo** (present/gift)
re-GA-lo

4) **mantél** (tablecloth)
man-TEL

5) **ang may kaarawán** (birthday person)
ang-may-ka-a-ra-WAN

6) **lóbo** (balloon)
LO-bo

7) **keyk páng-kaarawán** (birthday cake)
KEYK-PANG-ka-a-ra-WAN

8) **pláto** (plates)
PLA-to

9) **tinidór** (forks)
ti-ni-DOR

10) **kutsára** (spoons)
kut-SA-ra

11) **tása** (cups)
TA-sa

12) **istró** (straw)
is-TRO

13) **pabítin** (piñata)
pa-BI-tin

14) **kandílâ** (candle)
kan-DI-la

15) **sombréro** (hat)
som-BRE-ro

16) **bisíta** (guests)
bi-SI-ta

Nakatanggap ako ng maraming regalo para sa aking kaarawan.
I received a lot of gifts for my birthday.

Ang lahat ng mga bisita ay umalis na.
All the guests have gone.

Iginawa niya ako ng arko ng mga lobo.
She made me a balloon arch.

MGA MAGKASALUNGAT (OPPOSITES)

1) **malínis** (clean)
   ma-LI-nis

2) **marumí** (dirty)
   ma-ru-MI

3) **kauntî** (few)
   ka-un-TI

4) **marámi** (many)
   ma-RA-mi

5) **salákay** (attack)
   sa-LA-kay

6) **pagtatanggól** (defense)
   pag-ta-tang-GOL

7) **matuwíd** (straight)
   ma-tu-WID

8) **kurbádo** (curved)
   kur-BA-do

9) **magkasáma** (together)
   mag-ka-SA-ma

10) **magkáhiwaláy** (separated)
    mag-KA-hi-wa-LAY

11) **bátâ** (young)
    BA-ta

12) **matandâ** (old)
    ma-tan-DA

13) **kasaganáan** (wealth)
    ka-sa-ga-NA-an

14) **kakulangán** (shortage)
    ka-ku-la-NGAN

15) **malukóng** (concave)
    ma-lu-KONG

16) **malandáy** (convex)
    ma-lan-DAY

Ang aking mga magulang ay magkahiwalay.
My parents are separated.

Ako ang pinakabata.
I am the youngest.

Ang platong ito ay madumi.
This plate is dirty.

QUIZ #8

Use arrows to match the corresponding translations:

a. arrival

b. cheese

c. teddy bear

d. tourist guide

e. map

f. forks

g. grass

h. candle

i. doll

j. airport

k. truck

l. flowers

m. tent

n. mask

o. rice

p. candy

1. tolda

2. manika

3. bulaklak

4. trak

5. maskara

6. keso

7. kendi

8. paliparan

9. bigas

10. damo

11. tedi beyr

12. kard

13. pagdating

14. kandila

15. gabay ng turista

16. tinidor

Fill in the blank spaces with the options below (use each word only once):

Binisita ako ng pinsan kong si Coline para sa aking kaarawan. Ang biyahe niya ay isang tunay na bangungot! Umpisa pa lang ay hindi na siya nakuha ang _____ papuntang _____. Halos hindi niya naabot ang oras ng kaniyang _____. Sa kaniyang pagbaba sa eroplano, natanto niyang naiwan niya ang kanyang _____ sa paliparan na naglalaman ang kanyang pitaka kasama ang kanyang_____ at kaniyang_____. Pagdating sa _____, nakita niyang marami ang mga _____, na ang lahat ng mga kalye ay naharangan na ng trapiko . Gusto niyang tumigil upang bumili ng isang _____ ngunit hindi siya makahanap ng panaderya dahil nawala rin niya ang kanyang _____. Wala rin siyang regalo kaya tumigil siya sa tanging bukas na tindahan, na isang tindahan ng mga laruan, at bumili siya ng isang kyut na _____.

turista   keyk pang-kaarawán

kard ng pagkakakilanlan   pag-alis

bayan   gabay

paliparan   bitbit na bagahe

pasaporte   tedi beyr

paglipad   taksi

CONCLUSION

While there is certainly much more to say about the Tagalog language, we hope that this general overview will help you understand and use the words and phrases in this dictionary, as well as your own words and phrases, as you continue your journey to bilingualism.

We would like to leave you with a few suggestions for a pleasant and fruitful language learning experience:

1. Learn what you need and what you love.
   While survival Tagalog is indispensable, mechanical memorization of long lists of words is not the best use of your time and energy. Make sure to focus on the vocabulary that is important and useful to you in your life. Perhaps you need Tagalog for work or to visit family and friends. In this case, make sure you focus on the vocabulary that will be useful to reach these goals.

2. Do not skip learning grammar and tenses. Although it is not the most exciting part of learning a language, spending some time perfecting your grammar is the key to being able to manipulate the language in the long term.

3. Use available media, such as movies, music, and social media, to practice all aspects of the language. Provide the opportunity to practice reading, writing, and listening at any time from your phone or your computer. Aim to spend 20 minutes a day on your practice of the Tagalog language in order to make good progress.

4. Practice speaking with a native speaker as soon as you can. You can join speaking groups in real life or online.

5. Remember: **Communication before perfection**. It takes years to master a language, and fluency is not achieved easily. It requires commitment and regular practice. However, if you get to visit a Tagalog-speaking country, do not hesitate to try to speak Tagalog to everyone you meet. This will give you the motivation and the confidence to carry on learning. You might feel scared at first, but do not worry, people will be kind to you!

6. Enjoy the journey!

ANSWERS

QUIZ #1

a-13. b-11. c-10. d-15. e-9. f-12. g-6. h-14. i-8. j-1. k-5. l-2.
m-16. n-7. o-4. p-3.

Ang aking **ina** at ang aking ama ay hindi nagkasama sa loob ng ilang taon. Ang lahat ay laging **nagtataka** upang makita kung gaano silang nagkakasundo para sa **naghiwalay na mag-asawa**. Ang aking **kapatid na babae** ay ang aking matalik na kaibigan. Siya ay puno ng **kabaitan** at ito ay mayroong isang ginintuang **puso**. Para sa akin, ako ay **seryoso** at ang lahat ay nagsasabi na ako ay puno ng **katapangan**. Gustung-gusto ko ang mga hayop, lalo na ang mga aso. Bukas ng gabi ay inanyayahan kami sa bahay ng ama ko para maghapunan. Palagay ko ay maghahanda siya ng **pabo**. Sana ay gumanda ang pakiramdam ko dahil ngayon ay napakasakit ng aking **ulo** at **barado** ang aking ilong.

QUIZ # 2

a-10. b-5. c-8. d-9. e-2. f-13. g-15. h-16. i-3. j-12. k-1. l-4.
m-6. n-7. o-11. p-14.

Si Phil ay isang guro sa kindergarten. Noong nakaraang linggo, dinala niya ang kaniyang klase para bisitahin ang isang bukirin. Ayon sa ulat ng panahon, magiging maulan ngunit naging **maaraw** at napaka-**maalinsangan**. Nakasuot si Phil ng **maong** at amerikana. Naglalakad siya nang may **sapin sa paa**. Sa kasamaang-palad, hindi siya naging komportable sa buong maghapon. Sa pagbisita sa bukid, nakita ng mga bata ang mga baboy, kabayo at **baka**. Mayroon ding isang bahay-pukyutan na may daan-daang **bubuyog**. Sa kabilang banda, mayroon ding **putakti** at isa sa kanila ay kinagat si Phil!

180

QUIZ # 3

a-16.   b-14.   c-9.   d-8.   e-7.   f-11.   g-3.   h-5.   i-13.   j-12.   k-4.   l-2.
m-1.   n-15.   o-6   p-10.

Taglagas ang paborito kong panahon. Taun-taon, inaasahan ko ang Oktubre para **palamutian ang bakuran** at gayundin ang aking **balkonahe**. Ako at aking pamilya ay gustong-gusto ang **paghuhukay ng kalabasa** at inilalagay ang mga ito sa buong bahay. Lagi kong inilalagay ang isa sa harap ng **tsimeneya**. Nagmumukha ang mga itong maliliit at nakakatokatot na mga **ilawan**. Ang Oktubre 31 ay Halowin. Naglilibot kami para makakuha ng kendi mula sa mga kapitbahay. Pagkatapos niyon, sa pagsapit ng **hatinggabi**, nagpapa-ilaw kami ng **mga pinabangong kandila** at nagre-relaks sa **sopa** habang umiinom ng **mainit na tsokolate**. Naglalaro naman ang kapatid kong lalaki ng **video game**. Tuwing Nobyembre, uso ang **mag-iski** at pumunta para mag-iskeyting sa **ice rink** sa lungsod. Gustung-gusto ko ito!

QUIZ # 4

a-15.   b-7.   c-9.   d-13.   e-11.   f-10.   g-12.   h-14.   i-8.   j-2.   k-1.   l-16.
m-4.   n-5.   o-6.   p-3.

Si Gérald ay **mag-aaral** ng inhinyerong sibil sa Unibersidad ng Nantes. Siya ay nasa kanyang ikatlong taon. Kalaunan, gusto niyang maging **inhinyero** o **negosyante**. Ang kanyang mithiin ay maging mayaman at maglakbay sa mundo. Nangangarap siyang maglaro ng **balibol** sa isang **dalampasigan** sa Caribbean, bibili ng kanyang sariling **bangka** o mag- **jet ski** sa dagat. Ang paborito niyang **propesor** ay si G. Rendal. Siya ay napakatalino at karismatiko. Umaasa si Gerald na maging katulad niya kalaunan. Ngunit sa ngayon, kailangan niyang pumunta sa laundromat para gamitin ang **makinang panlaba** at labhan ang kanyang **maruming labada**. Bago iyon, kailangan niyang pumunta sa pamilihan para bumili ng **panlaba** at **pampalambot ng tela** dahil wala na siya ng mga ito.

QUIZ # 5

a-7.   b-3.   c-15   d-13.   e-12.   f-11.   g-2.   h-16.   i-14.   j-8.   k-6.   l-4.
m-5.   n-1.   o-10.   p-9.

Ang mga lolo't lola ko ay nakatira sa **Europa, kanluran** ng Copenhagen. Nagpasiya akong bisitahin sila sa susunod na buwan. Hindi namin madalas makita ang isa't isa dahil nakatira ako sa New York, ngunit salamat sa aking **kompyuter** at ang aking **webcam**. Ang lola ko ay isang mahusay na tagapagtugtog ng **piyano**. Dati-rati ay naglalaro siya nang live sa mga bar sa paligid ng lungsod. Siya ang nagturo sa akin na tumugtog ng **gitarang de koryente**!! Ang lolo ko ay **magsasaka**. Nagpapalago siya ng **usbong ng Bruselas** at mga prutas. Ginagawa niya ang pinakamainam na **mansanas** at **raspberi** na pie sa mundo.

QUIZ # 6

a-11. b-7. c-9. d-2. e-15. f-14. g-12. h-13. i-16. j-6. k-1. l-8.
m-3. n-4. o-5. p-10.

Nag-organisa ng masarap na handaan si Pauline at ang kanyang mga kaibigan matapos ang kanilang seremonya ng **pagtatapos** noong nakaraang katapusan ng linggo. Sa Setyembre, lahat sila ay pupunta para **magsimula sa unibersidad** maliban kay Pauline dahil gusto niyang **maglakbay sa buong mundo**. Siya ay papasok sa susunod pang taon. Ang menu ay napaka-**mahal**, ngunit ang pagkain ay sadyang nagkakahalaga ng ganito. Masarap iyon. Bilang pauna, mayroong **kabibe** at **alimango**. Masaya si Pauline dahil gustong-gusto niya ang pagkaing-dagat. Pagkatapos ay naroon ang pangunahing kurso. Nakapili sila sa pagitan ng **lasagna** at ng **manok** sa **mustasa**. Pinili ni Pauline ang manok ngunit sa kasamaang-palad ito ay medyo **matigas** at nagkulang ng **asin**. Para sa **panghimagas**, nagpakabusog sila sa isang masarap na tsokolateng fondant.

QUIZ # 7

a-14. b-11. c-13. d-15. e-12. f-6. g-5. h-1. i-16. j-9. k-4. l-7.
m-10. n-2. o-8. p-3.

Narito ang mga direksyon para makarating sa **tindahan ng damit**, mula sa lugar ng **fawnten**. Kailangan mong **lumiko** sa unang kalye sa **kanan** at pumunta sa **ilaw trapiko**. Kapag ang ilaw ay berde, lumiko sa kaliwa. **Sa likod** ng simbahan, mayroong isang istasyon ng **sabwey**. Bagtasin ang istasyon at ito ay magdadala sa iyo para **maglakad** sa loob ng 10 minuto. Makikita mo ang tindahan sa iyong kaliwa.

QUIZ # 8

a-13. b-6. c-11. d-15. e-12. f-16. g-10. h-14. i-2. j-8. k-4. l-3.
m-1. n-5. o-9. p-7.

Binisita ako ng pinsan kong si Coline para sa aking kaarawan. Ang biyahe niya ay isang tunay na bangungot! Umpisa pa alng ay hindi na siya nakakuha ng **taksi** papuntang **paliparan**. Halos hindi niya naabot ang oras ng kanyang **paglipad**. Sa kaniyang pagbaba sa eroplano, natanto niyang naiwan niya ang kanyang **bitbit na bagahe** sa paliparan na naglalaman ng kaniyang pitaka kasama ang kaniyang **pasaporte** at kaniyang **kard ng pagkakakilanlan**. Pagdating sa **bayan**, nakita niyang marami ang **mga turista,** na ang lahat ng mga kalye ay naharangan na ng trapiko. Gusto niyang tumigil upang bumili ng isang **keyk pang-kaarawan** ngunit hindi siya makahanap ng panaderya dahil nawala rin niya ang kanyang **gabay**. Wala rin siyang regalo, kaya tumigil siya sa tanging bukas na tindahan, na isang tindahan ng mga laruan, at bumili ng isang kyut na **tedi beyr.**

Made in United States
Troutdale, OR
01/21/2024

17052492R00106